C

SEMICONDUCTORS

U.S.A.:	BUTTERWORTH INC. WASHINGTON, D.C.: 7235 WISCONSIN AVENUE, 14
ENGLAND:	BUTTERWORTH & CO. (PUBLISHERS) LTD. LONDON: 88 KINGSWAY, W.C.2.
AUSTRALIA:	BUTTERWORTH & CO. (AUSTRALIA) LTD. SYDNEY: 6/8 O'CONNELL STREET MELBOURNE: 473 BOURKE STREET BRISBANE: 240 QUEEN STREET
CANADA:	BUTTERWORTH & CO. (CANADA) LTD. TORONTO: 1367 DANFORTH AVENUE, 6
NEW ZEALAND:	BUTTERWORTH & CO. (NEW ZEALAND) LTD. WELLINGTON: 49/51 BALLANCE STREET AUCKLAND: 35 HIGH STREET
SOUTH AFRICA:	BUTTERWORTH & CO. (SOUTH AFRICA) LTD. DURBAN: 33/35 BEACH GROVE

SEMICONDUCTORS

HORST TEICHMANN

Honorarprofessor an der Universität Würzburg

Translated by

L.F. SECRETAN, M.A.

WASHINGTON

BUTTERWORTHS

1964

Suggested U.D.C. Nos.: 537. 311. 33
Suggested additional Nos.: 621. 315. 592

Originally published under the title
Halbleiter
by **Bibliographisches Institut AG Mannheim**

© Bibliographisches Institut AG 1961

English Translation
©
Butterworth & Co. (Publishers) Ltd.
1964

Printed by The Lewes Press Wightman & Co. Ltd., Lewes, Sussex, England

FOREWORD TO ENGLISH TRANSLATION

There has been a steady flow of books on various aspects of electronic semiconductors during the last few years, some of a simple nature and some dealing with advanced aspects of the subject. Some of the short introductory texts fail to deal sufficiently with the basic modern physical ideas and others ignore applications of semiconductors in devices beyond the well known *p-n* junctions. The present volume is a translation of a text which has proved very popular in Germany where it was issued as a paperback. The translation has been carried out so as to preserve some of the flavour of the German original. The approach of the book is rather different from the smaller introductory texts printed in Britain and the U.S.A. and it is thought that students may benefit from a reading of a book based on this rather different approach and that the way will be paved for a study of more advanced general texts such as those by R. A. Smith and A. F. Ioffé or of specialist monographs.

C. A. Hogarth

CONTENTS

PREFACE

The purpose of this book is to bridge the gap between the literature which is strictly technical, tailored to practical applications, and that which is scientific and theoretical. It should serve as a textbook for both general and advanced students. Consequently it is not addressed to experts, but to those who are looking for something to lead them on to the specialized technical literature. When approaching a subject involving the study and application of physical phenomena to which he has hitherto paid little attention, the student is especially grateful for an introduction which assumes as little previous knowledge as possible; and on this fact of teaching experience this book is based.

Students who meet problems of semiconductors for the first time, as well as mature technologists now faced with problems which are new to them, both like to incorporate new knowledge into their existing frame of experience. In the case of semiconductors, this means connecting it with the basic physics and electrical engineering known when semiconduction phenomena were dismissed as 'impurity effects'.

This little book is therefore based on the electron theory of the electrical conductivity of metals, and presents a picture, in terms of both the particle and the wave theory, of the peculiarities of those substances which are known as electronic semiconductors.

For those readers who wish to go deeper into the subject, more detailed theoretical treatment is given in inset paragraphs, which can however be omitted without making the rest impossible to understand. For those readers who know very little about the concepts of wave mechanics, there is a brief introduction to its essential points, in so far as they are necessary for the understanding of semiconduction phenomena. There is a more detailed presentation in my

PREFACE

Einführung in die Atomphysik [Introduction to Atomic Physics], Volume 12 of this series [German paperback series].

I hope I have succeeded in achieving the objects outlined above, and that readers will find made clear many things which are new to them; and will also be able to make use of the information given in the tables.

I should like to thank my colleagues, Prof. H. Welker and Dr. L. Weiss, both of Siemens & Schuckert, Erlangen, for passing on reprints and making occasional suggestions. I am also grateful to Dr. B. Jansen, Philips Research Laboratories, Eindhoven, Netherlands, who was kind enough to let me have his original photographs of boundary layers and allow me to reproduce them. My former colleague Dr. H. Heinze, now of Allgemeine Deutsche Philips-Gesellschaft-Literaturstelle, Hamburg, has helped me with literature references, and I should like to thank him too. Mr. H. F. Ferbert, of Würzburg, has helped in the proof-reading, and my dear wife has helped with the preparation of the manuscript. I should finally like to thank the publishers; it has been a pleasure to collaborate with them in the production of this book, and they have considered all my wishes as to printing and layout.

HORST TEICHMANN

Nürnberg, Easter 1961

INTRODUCTION

The science of semiconductors illustrates, as does scarcely any other applied field, the many-sidedness of the concepts of theoretical physics which are used to interpret the results of experiment. In hardly any other field is it so necessary to distinguish the actual processes, of which, with our present methods of measurement, experiments can only give us a distorted picture, from the hypothetical picture which our conceptual framework—whether it be in a space-time continuum accessible to observation or in a configuration space—allows us to perceive. Only by keeping this always clearly in view, and being continually conscious of the nature of the similes employed in the very large number of separate concepts, whereby a whole range of properties illuminates a reality which cannot be experienced directly, is it possible to keep the necessary perspective to enable us, free from any preconceived ideas, to get closer to understanding the many physical peculiarities in the behaviour of semiconductors. Although they appear to be contradictory, both the particle and the wave theory have proved of service in enabling the processes of semiconduction to be understood. The antithesis between them has been very well expressed by von Weizsäcker as follows: 'The energy of a particle is concentrated at a point in space, where the particle is located: on the other hand, the energy of a wave, whose extension (with its field) in space is unbounded, is spread over the whole of space'. The significance of this sentence is that the two hypotheses cannot be combined and are in very truth antitheses. For one and the same phenomenon, the energy cannot both be condensed in one spot and spread over the whole of space at the same time. The mutually contradictory models provided by these two hypotheses can thus only be two different facets of a single reality, about which we can receive information in one form or the other, depending on the nature of the experiments we carry out.

As regards semiconductors, these two hypotheses give us, on the one hand, the explanation of their properties as an interaction between atoms (or ions) in a regular arrangement and quasi-free electrons (the particle picture), and, on the other hand, an explanation based on the behaviour of the material waves of electrons in the periodic potential field of crystal lattices, which leads to the 'band model' in the energy configuration space (wave picture). We shall see that both hypotheses complement each other in yielding knowledge of the characteristic features of the true behaviour of semiconductors; they show their heuristic value by fulfilling the criterion of a valid theory which was put forward by Hertz, namely, that the theoretical consequences of the hypotheses must correspond to the natural consequences of the observed phenomena. The description of the behaviour of semiconductors affords noteworthy examples of the validity of both hypotheses in this respect.

The technical applications of research into semiconductors have penetrated a very wide and varied field, extending from the application of the thermistor or NTC resistor as the operative element in the petrol gauge of a motor vehicle, via diodes and transistors, right across to low-noise amplifiers (masers) for radiotelescopes in astronomy and astronautics.

Development is far from being concluded, and at present is proceeding in the direction of ever smaller components (molecular electronics). The following chapters will show how closely interwoven are the fundamental physics and technology of semiconductors.

HISTORICAL SURVEY

AMONG the solids, one group of substances, the metals, shows very high values of electrical conductivity, while another group, the insulators, scarcely conducts electricity at all. The gap between these two groups is bridged by a series of substances known as semiconductors. Their electrical conductivities cover the wide range of 10^4 to 10^{-12} ohm^{-1} cm^{-1}, approximately, although these limits do not necessarily exclude a certain degree of arbitrariness. The electrical conductivity of semiconductors depends on so many factors that it has needed years of very intensive research to separate the effects due to each one individually. Until the 1920s, therefore, the physics of semiconductors was bedevilled by impurities, and perpetually troubled by inaccuracy. The fact that the first known semiconductor was the element selenium (Se), which can still surprise physicists by its various crystalline modifications and the difficulty of preparing it in the pure state, may have considerably contributed to this state of affairs. One of the surprises of selenium was the discovery of an autonomous photoelectric e.m.f., which was described by C. F. Fritts as long ago as the 1870s. Even then, the significance of this discovery was fully realized, and Siemens expressed it in the following words (which may be read in the reports of the meetings of the Prussian Academy of Sciences): 'We are here concerned with an entirely new physical phenomenon, of the very greatest scientific importance . . . because for the first time we are faced with the direct transformation of light into electrical energy'. However, efforts to control and reproduce this phenomenon failed, and it sank once more into oblivion. The same thing happened with unipolar conductivity, i.e. conductivity which depends on the direction of the current, which was also observed at a very early date in selenium connected to metal contacts. The only one of these early discoveries about selenium which was not forgotten was the fact that its conductivity changes when light falls on it. In the following period, therefore, selenium was used only as a photoresistor. The positive temperature coefficient of electrical conductance (or negative temperature coefficient of resistance) observed in selenium, i.e. the increase in conductivity (decrease in resistivity) with rising temperature, was for a long time considered, quite generally, as the criterion of a semiconductor as opposed to a metal, whose conductivity behaves in the opposite way with changing temperature, until a series of compounds became known—e.g. borides, carbides and nitrides—whose structure corresponds to that of a semiconductor but whose conductivity changes with temperature in the same way as that of a metal. Nowadays, semiconductors with positive temperature coefficients of conductance are called, in technology, thermistors or NTC resistors on account of their applications as temperature-dependent resistors. In the course of a search for a less ambiguous distinguishing characteristic of semiconductors than their temperature coefficient of conductance, the physical basis of the processes which take place in them was finally found with the discovery of a series of substances whose physical behaviour showed the reproducibility so sadly lacking in selenium. This includes primarily cuprous oxide (Cu_2O), to which germanium (Ge) and silicon (Si) were later added, and, most recently, the $A^{III}B^V$ compounds, i.e. compounds of elements of the third and fifth columns of the periodic table, like, for instance, GaAs and InSb. In the 1920s, the unipolar conductivity of layers of cuprous oxide grown on the parent copper formed the basis for the construction of practical copper oxide rectifiers, in which both Schottky, in the Siemens Research Laboratories, and Lange, in what was then known as the Kaiser Wilhelm Institute for Silicate Research, simultaneously and independently, in 1928, observed the phenomenon of the production of a photoelectric e.m.f. in the presence of light, which had been observed in selenium half a century earlier. The same photoelectric phenomenon

2

also occurs with germanium and silicon, and has recently led to the construction of very efficient photocells, which can, for example, be grouped into a 'solar battery' to provide a source of current for artificial satellites.

In electrical conduction in these semiconductors (Cu_2O, Ge, Si, $A^{III}B^V$ compounds), what carries the charge? This question can be fully answered from a knowledge of the Hall effect (*see* p. 19), and once again the answer is: the electrons. Because of the outstanding importance of semiconductors which have electronic conductance, only they will be dealt with. Semiconducting substances which, according to the some-what arbitrary classification by conductivity at the beginning of this chapter, also fall under the general heading of semi-conductors but show ionic conductance, having been exten-sively studied by R. W. Pohl and his co-workers, will therefore be excluded from further mention here. We shall first, there-fore, give a short account of the electron theory of the electrical behaviour of metals, and then show how phenomena observed in electronic semiconductors can be described by a generalized treatment according to electron theory, and how this treatment, in which equal use is made of the particle and wave hypotheses, enables a sharp distinction to be drawn between metals, on the one hand, and semiconductors and insulators on the other; from which it will follow that the behaviour of these two latter groups does not differ sharply, but by gradual stages.

3

THE ELECTRON AS PARTICLE AND WAVE

ELECTRICAL charges are carried by electrons and ions, and it is the movement of these particles to which the phenomenon of electrical conductivity is attributed. Ions are electrically charged atoms, so that their movement always involves the transport of matter, whereas the electrons carry scarcely any matter, for they have only one-1,837th part of the mass of a hydrogen atom. It is to the electrons and their interaction with each other and with matter on which the explanation of the electrical phenomena observed in metals and electronic semiconductors depends.

The definition of an electron states that it has a very small negative charge, which cannot be subdivided and which has the value e of the elementary electric charge, that—as previously mentioned—its mass is tiny, and that—in so far as it is assumed to be spherical—it possesses an extremely small radius. The values of these quantities are:

$$e = 1 \cdot 60.10^{-19} \text{ C}$$

$$m_e = 9 \cdot 11.10^{-28} \text{ g} \qquad \ldots . (2.1)$$

$$r_e = 2 \cdot 81.10^{-13} \text{ cm}$$

To this concept of the electron as a particle may be opposed the concept of the electron as a wave, which is equally well founded experimentally. For if a beam of electrons is directed towards the regularly arranged atomic lattice of a metallic substance (against the face of a single crystal of nickel, for instance), the beam of electrons is found—as Davisson and Germer showed in the year 1927—to be not simply reflected,

ELECTRON AS PARTICLE AND WAVE

as would be expected of a beam of particles, but split into a series of different rays of different intensities and different angles of reflection; a phenomenon such as is only observed in the diffraction of light by gratings and of x-rays by crystals. The results of this and of a series of similar experiments led to the electron being also attributed with the nature of a wave; such waves are called material waves. The way in which they behave forms the subject of wave mechanics, which was founded and developed by de Broglie (1924) and Schrödinger (1927) (cf. p. 42). According to this, an electron which passes through a potential difference of $U = 150$ V in an electric field will acquire a wave-length λ_ϵ of about 10^{-8} cm (1 Å). Here one has the wave hypothesis of the electron, in addition to, and just as correct as, the explanation of the electrical behaviour of electronic conductors based on the particle model of the electron. This wave hypothesis will serve particularly well in explaining the conduction behaviour of semiconductors, which —as is already known—differs considerably from that of metals.

In analytical mechanics, the behaviour of a particle is determined when its energy E and its momentum J are known. In physical optics, a wave is described by its frequency ν and its wave-length λ. The work of Planck and Einstein on the quantum theory of light led to the following relations between the particle and wave data for light:

$$E = h\nu, \qquad J = \frac{h\nu}{c} \qquad \ldots (2.2a)$$

where $h = 6 \cdot 62.10^{-27}$ erg sec is Planck's constant and $c = 3.10^{10}$ cm sec^{-1} is the velocity of light. The wave-length of the light is therefore given by $\lambda = c/\nu$.

De Broglie applied the conditions for light quanta (2.2a) to particles, observing that the velocity of a particle is a velocity of propagation, not a phase velocity (as with light). He therefore based his wave mechanics on the relations:

$$E = h\nu; \qquad J = \frac{h}{\lambda} \qquad \ldots (2.2b)$$

B

From the second of these equations, putting $J = mv$, the wave-length λ of matter may be calculated as:

$$\lambda = \frac{h}{\sqrt{2mE}} \qquad \dots (2.3)$$

Putting $m = m_e$ and $E = eU$ (U is the potential difference through which the electron must pass to acquire a kinetic energy $E = \frac{1}{2}m_e v^2$) gives, with equation 2.3, the material wave-length λ_e of the electron.

The electronic nature of electrical conductivity may be demonstrated either by the Hall effect or by the Tolman experiment. In the Hall effect, the carriers of electric charge are deflected by a transverse magnetic field in such a way that one side of the conductor becomes more charged than the other, and the sign of the difference in charge is an indication of the sign of the charge of the carriers of the electricity, while the amount of the difference in charge is an indication of the concentration of the carriers. The difference in charge is measured in the form of the Hall voltage. With electronic conduction, to which the assumptions made in *Figure 1b* about the direction of the current and field refer, a negative potential is measured at the lower edge.

Figure 1a represents the interaction between a uniform magnetic field and the circular magnetic field which surrounds an electron in motion. With the assumptions made in the diagram, there will be an increase in the intensity of the uniform magnetic field above the electron, and a decrease in its intensity below. This causes the electron to be deflected in the direction of decreasing field strength, i.e. leads to a curvature of its path. This behaviour is in every way analogous to the phenomenon in flow theory (aerodynamics and hydrodynamics) of the superimposition of laminar (uniform) flow on circular flow. In this case, analogous to the drop in field strength, there is a drop in pressure in the direction in which the source of the circular flow (the eddy) moves. In flowing round the profile of the supporting wing, this drop in pressure provides the lifting force for the aircraft; circulation of air caused by a rotating cylinder (the Flettner rotor) produces, by interaction with wind flow, a force which can be utilized for forward motion. Experiments to construct a cheap form of propulsion for ships in this way have foundered on the large surface area which Flettner rotors present to the stronger currents of air.

Figure 1b explains the occurrence of the Hall voltage on the basis of the theory developed in *Figure 1a* regarding the behaviour of electrons in a transverse magnetic field. It can be shown to be proportional to the width of the conductor, the current density and the magnetic field

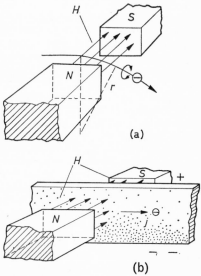

(a)

(b)

Figure 1. Electron and magnetic field: (a) Movement of an electron in a magnetic field; (b) The Hall effect in electronic conductivity

strength. The factor of proportionality, R_H, is called the Hall coefficient. The Hall coefficient is a constant of the material, and depends on the specific electrical properties of the substance in question. It is obvious that a given magnetic field can affect the current carriers in the substance, i.e. deflect them, more easily, the lower their concentration and the smaller their charges. It is therefore expected that the Hall coefficient be inversely proportional to the charge (e, for the electron) and to the concentration n of the current carriers in the substance. And in fact, electron theory gives, to a first approximation, the value:

$$R_H = \frac{1}{en} \text{ or more exactly } R_H = \frac{3\pi}{8} \frac{1}{en} \quad \ldots . (2.4)$$

for the Hall coefficient. If e is replaced by the value of the elementary electric charge (1), the measurement of R_H gives the concentration n of electrons in the substance in question. For metals, this value is of the order of $n \sim 10^{23}$ cm^{-3}. This agrees with an estimate based on the following considerations.

In one gram atom of a metal (e.g. copper, with atomic weight $A = 63\cdot57$) there are, from Avogadro's number, $N = 6\cdot02.10^{23}$ atoms. Since the density of copper is $8\cdot9$ g cm^{-3}, the concentration of copper atoms n_{Cu} may be calculated to be:

$$n_{Cu} = \frac{8\cdot9.6\cdot02}{63\cdot57} .10^{23} = 8.10^{22} \text{ cm}^{-3} \quad \ldots . (2.5)$$

Since copper is monovalent, i.e. it possesses one valence electron per atom in a relatively loose bond, it may fairly be assumed that for each atom, one electron is available to conduct electricity. The result of this estimate shows satisfactory agreement with the value for the concentration of electrons which was obtained from the Hall effect, and, vice versa, the results of the calculation from the Hall effect can be seen as experimental confirmation of the assumption that in monovalent metals the valence electrons determine metallic conduction and move 'quasi-freely' through the crystal lattice of the metal. For semiconductors, measurements of the Hall effect yield figures for the electron concentration of the order of $n = 10^{14}$ to 10^{18} cm^{-3}. This suggests that the electrons are made available for carrying the charge in a different way from that in metals. In any case, the fact that the concentrations are considerably lower than in metals (*see* equation 2.5) must make this more difficult.

In the Tolman experiment, a coil of copper wire is made to revolve very fast and is then suddenly stopped (*Figure 2*). The charge carriers in the coil of copper wire, enclosed in the crystal lattice of the metal and moving at the same speed as the atoms of which the copper wire consists, are flung out

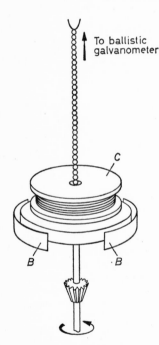

To ballistic galvanometer

Figure 2. Diagram of the Tolman experiment (C—rotating coil, B—block brakes)

of their equilibrium positions on this sudden braking, causing a measurable pulse of current in an external circuit. This pulse of current is measured by means of a ballistic galvanometer. Its sign also tells us the sign of the charge carriers, and the size of the deflection enables their specific charge (meaning charge per unit mass) to be calculated. Inserting the values for the electron given in equation 2.1, we get, for its specific charge, the value: $e/m_e = 1.76 \cdot 10^8$ Cg^{-1}. For metals and electronic semiconductors, the Tolman experiment gives values which agree within the limits of experimental error.

The apparatus is shown, diagrammatically only, in *Figure 2*. Clearly there are many possible sources of error which must be eliminated: first, the effect of the earth's magnetic field, which is compensated for by a coil—not shown in *Figure 2*— and secondly, contact resistances when making an electrically conducting connection between the rotating coil and the ballistic galvanometer. The use of sliding contacts had therefore to be dispensed with, and the experiment carried out in a sort of tower in which the input leads could twist during the rotation.

To calculate the specific charge in the Tolman experiment, we may proceed as follows:

The electrons acquire a velocity v by rotation. By braking for a time t they suffer a deceleration $b = -v/t$, to which they oppose a moment of inertia $-m_e v/t$. This causes a pulse of current $i.t$ which is shown on the ballistic galvanometer. The electron current $-i$ causes a drop in voltage $U = -iW$ in the conductor circuit, of which W represents the resistance. This results in a field strength of U/l in a conductor of length l (length of winding in the rotating coil). This exerts a force of eU/l on each electron which counteracts the inertia of the electrons. They can only continue moving until the force of the field and the moment of inertia are in equilibrium. Then:

$$e \frac{U}{l} = e \frac{-i.W}{l} = -m_e \frac{v}{t} \qquad \ldots \ldots (2.6a)$$

from whence it follows that:

$$\frac{e}{m_e} = \frac{l.v}{W.i.t} \qquad \ldots \ldots (2.6b)$$

ELECTRON AS PARTICLE AND WAVE

When these experiments had succeeded in clarifying the electronic nature of the conductivity of metals and of a large group of semiconductors, it became possible to lay the foundations of the electron theory of the electrical behaviour of these substances, as will be shown.

THE ELECTRON THEORY OF ELECTRICAL CONDUCTION

THE solids with which we are now concerned are all crystal-line in structure, i.e. they normally form aggregates of crystals —in the ideal case, single crystals—each made up by the regular repetition of very small unit cells. Take once more the metal, copper, as an example. Its unit cell consists of a cube with copper atoms at the corners and at the intersections of the diagonals of the faces. The length of one edge of this elementary cube of the 'cubic' lattice of copper is called the 'lattice constant' a_{Cu} and is $3 \cdot 61.10^{-8}$ cm. But only at very low temperatures will the copper atoms be found at rest at these sites. At normal temperatures, say at room temperature ($T \sim 300°$ K), they will perform oscillations about these rest positions. The copper atom consists of a nucleus with a charge of $+29e$ (atomic number 29), surrounded by 29 electrons arranged in shells. The outermost shell—which in the copper atom is called the N shell—contains only one electron. This electron is the most loosely bound to the nucleus, because the K, L and M shells, which are full of electrons, screen the charge on the nucleus from it. This 'valence electron' also determines the valency properties of the (monovalent) element copper in chemical compounds. Since it is so loosely bound, it can easily break away from the atomic bond and move independently and 'quasi-freely' through the lattice of copper atoms—or, to be exact, copper ions, since the valence electrons have been lost. The energy to release these electrons comes, first, from the heat of the surroundings, and, secondly, from the crystal lattice of copper, which is so constituted that the potential fields of the individual copper ions lie superimposed alternately, which tends to weaken the bonds of the valence electrons at the separate points of the lattice. Consequently, the electrons move almost as freely through the crystal lattice of copper as do the molecules of a gas in an enclosed space, and we speak of an 'electron gas'. The thermal motion of the copper atoms (or ions), that is, their oscillation about their rest positions, helps to weaken the bonds of the valence electrons. There will therefore be more charged particles available at high temperatures than at low temperatures. In thermal equilibrium, that is to say, in the stationary state, electrons are continually being captured by the lattice and others are being re-emitted, so that on the average there are just as many free, or, rather, 'quasi-free', electrons per unit volume of metal as there are atoms, i.e. the concentration of electrons will be about 10^{23} cm^{-3}, as has already been discussed (p. 8). The electrons participate in the thermal motion and move about rapidly in the crystal lattice. There are, on the average, equal numbers of electrons moving in each direction across any given section, so that no difference of potential can be observed between different parts of the crystal. This picture of quasi-free electrons may be taken as the basis of our explanation of the electrical behaviour of metals.

The thermal motion is responsible for a process which we call 'diffusion'; whereby, as soon as the thermal equilibrium is disturbed, a balancing process takes place which attempts to restore it. Einstein arrived at an important relationship concerning the diffusion of charged particles, and this is now deduced.

Suppose that, in a metal rod of section $q = 1$ cm^2 and length x, the concentration gradient of the electrons at a given point is dn/dx. By the thermal balancing process, the electrons will move down the concentration gradient, diffusing from the points of higher concentration to those of lower concentration. The electron gas expands, following the gradient dp/dx of the pressure of the electron gas. The equation of state for gases enables this to be calculated:

$$p = \frac{R.T}{V} = \frac{N}{V}.k.T = n.k.T \qquad \dots \text{(3.1a)}$$

Here R is the universal gas constant, N the number of electrons in volume V, $k = R/N = 1 \cdot 38.10^{-16}$ erg/deg is Boltzmann's constant, and T the absolute temperature. From equation 3.1a it follows that the pressure gradient, the force expanding the electron gas, which is the basis of diffusion, is given by:

$$\frac{\mathrm{d}p}{\mathrm{d}x} = k.T.\frac{\mathrm{d}n}{\mathrm{d}x} \qquad \dots (3.1b)$$

Since the particles which diffuse are electrons, i.e. charged, there will also be an electrical force, arising from the potential difference U which results from the difference in concentration, since the region where the electron concentration is high is more negatively charged than that where the electron concentration is low. If the field strength of the potential field U is F, then the force K acting on one electron will have the value $K = eF$; and the force acting on N electrons will be $K = NeF$. If the velocity of an electron is denoted by v and its mobility (velocity in field strength unity) by $\mu = v/F$, then the electrical force K which acts on the diffusing electron gas can be written

$$K = Nve/\mu \qquad \dots (3.2a)$$

The product Nv, the number of particles M moving per unit time, represents the change in the number of electrons per unit time, $\mathrm{d}M/\mathrm{d}t$. But Fick's law of diffusion gives this as:

$$Nv = \frac{\mathrm{d}M}{\mathrm{d}t} = D.q.\frac{\mathrm{d}n}{\mathrm{d}x} \qquad \dots (3.2b)$$

in which D is the diffusion coefficient. We have assumed initially that $q = 1$, so that, substituting from equation 3.2b in equation 3.2a, we get

$$K = \frac{De}{\mu} \cdot \frac{\mathrm{d}n}{\mathrm{d}x} \qquad \dots (3.2c)$$

In a state of thermal equilibrium, there must be equilibrium between the temperature-conditioned pressure

14

THEORY OF ELECTRICAL CONDUCTION

gradient of the electron gas (the force of diffusion) dp/dx (equation 3.1b) and the electrical force (equation 3.2c), so that

$$\frac{D}{\mu} = \frac{kT}{e} \qquad \ldots (3.3a)$$

This is Einstein's law when the electron gas is in a state of thermal equilibrium. Each side has the dimensions of a potential U_T. This is the potential up to which the electron can accumulate thermal energy. For $T = 300°$ K, this potential has the value $U_T = -29$ mV.

There is a simple relation between the mobility μ and the conductivity σ, or the resistivity $1/\sigma = \rho$. The conductivity is given by the flow of charged particles through unit cross-section per unit time in a field of unit strength. We therefore have:

$$\sigma = ne\mu \qquad \ldots (3.3b)$$

By means of equation 2.4, it is found that the mobility is the product of the electrical conductivity and the Hall coefficient R_H:

$$\mu = \sigma R_H \quad \text{or} \quad \mu = \frac{R_H}{\rho} \qquad \ldots (3.3c)$$

The mobilities can therefore be determined by measuring the electrical conductivity and the Hall coefficients. For electronic semiconductors they are of the order of 1 to 10^4 cm^2/V s (cf. Table 4, pp. 74–75).

In a field of strength F, a charged particle will acquire a velocity v in the period between its thermal excitation and its recombination, i.e. during its life τ.

$$v = \tfrac{1}{2} \frac{e}{m_e} F\tau \qquad \ldots (3.3d)$$

and the mobility of the particle will be given by

$$\mu = \tfrac{1}{2} \frac{e}{m_e} \tau \qquad \ldots (3.3e)$$

15

Since the mobility is inversely proportional to the mass, it follows that heavier particles (e.g. ions) will move more slowly than electrons having the same life. When we come to discuss the movement of carriers of charge in the periodic field of the lattice potential, we shall draw an interesting conclusion from this (cf. p. 76).

During its life τ the charged particle covers a path which is known as its diffusion length L. A connection can be found between L, τ and the diffusion coefficient D by considering the quantity of particles diffusing through an element of volume. The excess of particles entering this element over particles leaving it must be proportional to the change in their number with time, or

$$D\frac{\mathrm{d}^2 n}{\mathrm{d}x^2} = \frac{\mathrm{d}n}{\mathrm{d}t} \qquad \ldots (3.3\text{f})$$

This is Fick's law of diffusion. If Δn denotes the small number of particles diffusing in time τ, then we can put $\mathrm{d}n/\mathrm{d}t = \Delta n/\tau$ and equation 3.3f becomes:

$$D\frac{\mathrm{d}^2}{\mathrm{d}x^2}(\Delta n) - \frac{\Delta n}{\tau} = 0 \qquad \ldots (3.3\text{g})$$

of which the solution is:

$$\Delta n = \Delta n\,(0)\,\mathrm{e}^{-x/\sqrt{D\tau}} = \Delta n\,(0)\,\mathrm{e}^{-x/L}$$

from which it follows that L, the diffusion length when the quantity diffusing has dropped to $1/e$ of its initial value, is given by:

$$L = \sqrt{D\tau} \qquad \ldots (3.3\text{h})$$

The diffusion lengths of electronic semiconductors lie between 10^{-1} and 10^{-4} cm (cf. Table 4, pp. 74–75).

The actual diffusion coefficient D, which has hitherto been assumed to be constant, does actually vary considerably with temperature according to the Boltzmann distribution law (equation 3.5c), viz.:

$$D = D_0\,\mathrm{e}^{\cdot\,\mathscr{E}/kT} \qquad \ldots (3.3\text{i})$$

THEORY OF ELECTRICAL CONDUCTION

in which D_0 is the diffusion coefficient extrapolated to $T = \infty$ and $\mathcal{E}$ is, for electrons, the potential energy in the crystalline lattice; or, in the case of the diffusion of lattice bricks (atoms or ions), the energy of their lattice bond.

If a voltage is applied to the ends of a copper wire, the electrons moving rapidly around in the wire with their thermal kinetic energies will receive an overall component of velocity in the direction of the electric field, that is to say, on the average more electrons will move towards the direction of the positive potential than towards the negative potential. This accounts for a flow of electrical charges, electric conduction. The way in which electric conduction in metals depends on temperature can then be explained as follows. When the metal is heated, it receives thermal energy, some of which— as already explained—goes to produce more charged particles; but some also goes to increase the amplitude of oscillation of the metal ions about their rest positions. This increase in amplitude tends to hinder the movement of the electrons in the direction of the field. Since at normal temperatures $(T \sim 300°\ \mathrm{K})$ scarcely any of the valence electrons remain bonded to the atoms, but lead a quasi-free existence, a rise in temperature has more effect in hindering the movement of the electrons than in increasing their number. This makes itself felt in an increase in resistance, or decrease in conductance, which explains the positive temperature coefficient of resistance (or negative coefficient of conductance) of metals.

The Wiedemann–Franz–Lorenz relation between the electrical conductivity σ, the thermal conductivity (heat conductivity) κ and the absolute temperature T, which is strictly obeyed and accurately proved by experiment, is:

$$\frac{\kappa}{\sigma T} = C_{\mathrm{WFL}} \qquad \ldots . (3.4a)$$

The Wiedemann–Franz–Lorenz constant C_{WFL} has the nature of a universal constant and its value has been very accurately determined for metals experimentally:

$$C_{\mathrm{WFL}} = 2\cdot72.10^{-13}\ \mathrm{g\ s^{-2}\ deg.^{-2}} \qquad \ldots . (3.4b)$$

The deduction of this value from the various models of

17

electron theory furnishes a proof of the correctness of the basic assumptions of these models of electrical conduction, which differ in the way they take account of the velocity of the electrons.

Drude's theory starts by assuming that all the electrons move with the same mean velocity, and it enables the constant C_{WFL} to be expressed by means of two universal constants whose values are already known, namely Boltzmann's constant k and the elementary quantum of electricity (the electronic charge) e. It gives the value

$$C_{WFL} = 3 \left(\frac{k}{e} \right)^2 = 2 \cdot 18.10^{-13} \text{ g s}^{-2} \text{ deg.}^{-2} \quad \ldots (3.4c)$$

Lorenz assumed that in conduction the velocities of the electrons have a Boltzmann distribution, and this gives the value

$$C_{WFL} = 2 \left(\frac{k}{e} \right)^2 = 1 \cdot 45.10^{-13} \text{ g s}^{-2} \text{ deg.}^{-2} \quad \ldots (3.4d)$$

for the constant. Comparing the values 3.4b, 3.4c and 3.4d of C_{WFL} it is seen that the better basic assumption leads to worse agreement between the theoretical and experimental values. Undoubtedly any improved theory must include a distribution of velocities, but obviously the Boltzmann distribution is not suitable for explaining conduction in metals.

Sommerfeld therefore sought to explain electronic conduction in metals by assuming a different velocity distribution, namely a Fermi form. This gives a value for the constant C_{WFL} which shows extremely good numerical agreement with the value found experimentally (3.4b):

$$C_{WFL} = \frac{\pi^2}{3} \left(\frac{k}{e} \right)^2 = 2 \cdot 68.10^{-13} \text{ g s}^{-2} \text{ deg.}^{-2} \quad \ldots (3.4e)$$

We shall return later to the physical differences between the Boltzmann and Fermi velocity distributions (cf. p. 31). The flow of a current of electricity, or, in our model, the movement of electrons towards more positive potentials, also results in collisions taking place between electrons and the ions in the lattice, in which energy which the electrons have received from the applied electric field is given up to the ions of the lattice, thus increasing their amplitude of oscillation about their rest positions. The energy absorbed by the ions of the lattice makes itself evident in a rise in temperature. This heat resulting from the passage of an electric current is called the Joule heat. It is immediately obvious that this Joule heat will be proportional to the square of the current strength, for the number of collisions is proportional to both the number of colliding particles (electrons) and the number of particles with which they collide (ions). Since, as has already been mentioned (*see* pp. 8 and 13), the concentration of electrons can be assumed to be equal to the concentration of ions, the fact that there are equal numbers of both types of colliding partners means that the heat developed will be proportional to the square of the current strength. Our hypothesis about the electronic nature of electrical conduction therefore explains Joule's law as well.

An external magnetic field will, according to its direction—transverse or longitudinal—influence the length of path of the electrons. As discussed previously (cf. p. 7), a transverse field leads to the Hall effect. A longitudinal magnetic field forces the electrons—unless by chance they happen to be moving in exactly the same direction as the magnetic lines of force—to move in helical paths, thus increasing the length of their path and increasing the number of collisions with the ions of the lattice, which will appear to the observer as an increase in resistance (decrease in conductance). This phenomenon is known as the Thomson effect, and can be utilized, for example, in the measurement of magnetic fields. But a thermal current, or flow of heat, can also give rise to electrical effects under the influence of a transverse or longitudinal magnetic field. Table 1 gives the whole group of electromagnetic and thermomagnetic effects with diagrams of how they arise. Depending on whether the motion of the electrons is thought of as being primarily caused by an electric field or a temperature gradient, the electromagnetic or thermomagnetic effects in transverse or longi-

Table 1. Summary of Electromagnetic and Thermomagnetic Effects and Their Laws

Effect	Magnetic field		
	Transverse	Longitudinal	
Electromagnetic, primarily electric current $i_e \left(= \sigma \dfrac{U_2 - U_1}{l}\right)$	Hall effect: transverse potential difference $\Delta_e U_{tr} = R_H b \cdot j_e H$	Thomson effect: longitudinal voltage difference; change in electrical conductance $\Delta_e U_l = K \cdot l \cdot j_e H^2$	Nernst effect: longitudinal temperature difference $\Delta_e T_l = L \cdot l \cdot j_e H$
	Ettingshausen effect: transverse temperature difference $\Delta_e T_{tr} = P \cdot b \cdot j_e H$		
Thermomagnetic, primarily thermal current $j_{th} \left(= \kappa \dfrac{T_2 - T_1}{l}\right)$	Nernst (Ettingshausen) effect: transverse potential difference $\Delta_{th} U_{tr} = Q \cdot b \times \dfrac{T_2 - T_1}{l} \cdot H$	Ettingshausen–Nernst effect: longitudinal potential difference $\Delta_{th} U_l = N \cdot d \times \dfrac{T_2 - T_1}{l} \cdot H$	Maggi-Righi-Leduc effect: longitudinal temperature difference: change in thermal conductance $\Delta_{th} T_l = M \cdot l \times \dfrac{T_2 - T_1}{l} \cdot H^2$
	Righi–Leduc effect: transverse temperature difference $\Delta_{th} T_{tr} = S \cdot b \times \dfrac{T_2 - T_1}{l} \cdot H$		
Diagrams of experiments l—length, b—breadth, d—thickness } of conductor			

tudinal magnetic fields will lead to longitudinal or transverse differences in potential or temperature. Of these effects, those named after Hall and Thomson have found particular application in technology (cf. pp. 116 and 120).

According to the electron theory, the difference between two different metals having different conductivities lies in the different concentrations of electron gas, which are of the same order of magnitude but differ in value. For example, the rough calculation already carried out for copper (*see* p. 8) gave the value $n_{Cu} = 8.10^{22}$ cm^{-3}, and for silver would give $n_{Ag} = 6.10^{22}$ cm^{-3}. If a conducting circuit is made from two different substances, there will be two points of contact between the faces of substances having differing concentrations of electrons. At these boundary surfaces, corresponding to the concentration gradient, an exchange of electrons will take place by diffusion, which causes the substance whose concentration of electrons is initially the lower to become more negative than the other, until no further exchange of electrons occurs. The potential difference set up at the boundary surface in the stationary state corresponds to the contact potential. In a closed conducting circuit the contact potentials at both boundary faces will compensate each other.

To calculate the diffusion potential which gives rise to the contact potential difference, we start by remembering that the diffusion process is based on energy which is thermal in origin and which—as shown above (cf. p. 15), (equation 3.3a)—enables the electrons to move against the potential $U_T = kT/e$. In the state of thermal equilibrium, therefore, U_T corresponds to the electron concentration $n(T)$. A change in electron concentration dn must therefore correspond to a change in potential $-dU$, which the change in concentration tries to reverse. We may therefore write:

$$n(T) : U_T = dn : -dU \qquad \ldots (3.5a)$$

It follows that

$$\frac{dn}{n} = -\frac{1}{U_T} dU \qquad \ldots (3.5b)$$

or, by integrating the differential equation and substituting from equation 3.3a,

$$n = n_0 \, e^{-U/U_T} = n_0 \, e^{-\frac{U}{D/\mu}} = n_0 \, e^{-eU/kT} \quad \ldots (3.5c)$$

The contact potential difference U_{12} between two substances having electron concentrations n_1 and n_2 will therefore be given by:

$$U_{12} = -(U_1 - U_2) = U_T \ln n_1/n_2 \quad \ldots (3.5d)$$

when $n_1 > n_2$. Since, as a rule, the ratio of the electron concentrations is between 1 and 3, we can of course put the logarithm approximately equal to 1. Since $U_T = -29$ mV, the approximate value of the contact potentials will be

$$U_{12} = 0.03 \text{ V} \quad \ldots (3.5e)$$

This value is of the order of magnitude of the values of contact potentials which have been measured for semiconductors. The values of the contact potentials for metals, however, have been found experimentally to be about 20 times as great. For the first time, we have found that the theory we have been using does not agree with the facts. The modifications it needs will be discussed later (cf. pp. 31 ff.).

Equation 3.5c sets out an interesting connection between the electron concentration n on the one hand and the energy of the electrons eU and the absolute temperature T on the other. This is known in physics as the Boltzmann distribution, and is often used in electron theory—particularly for semiconductors. We shall frequently have occasion to come back to it, and shall write it in the form

$$n = n_0 \, e^{-E/kT} \quad \ldots (3.5f)$$

in which $E = eU$ is used as a general expression for the energy of a particle (electron).

The way in which the electron concentration depends on temperature frequently differs in two different conductors. If in a conducting circuit like that in *Figure 3* one junction is made hotter than the other, different states of equilibrium will therefore be reached at the two junctions. But since these, being connected by a conductor, cannot exist together without an equalization of charge, an electric current will flow in

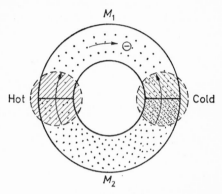

Figure 3. Thermoelectric circuit (M_1, M_2—substances having different electronic conductivities)

the circuit, the thermoelectric current, arising from the thermoelectric potential. This in its turn is due to the difference in temperature between the junctions, causing a difference in their contact potential differences. The thermoelectric current causes the electron gas to expand at the hot junction and to contract at the cold junction, relative to the state of equilibrium which would exist if the junctions were at the same temperature. As is known from the theory of heat, the expansion of a gas always causes cooling, and the compression of a gas causes heating, and this means that the thermoelectric effect (known as the Seebeck effect after its discoverer) results in a cooling of the hot junction and heating of the cold junction, by the reverse process, in an attempt to restore the state of equilibrium. This reverse effect was first described by Peltier, and is called, after him, the Peltier effect. The current which gives rise to the Peltier effect can also come from an external source, so that the effect can be used to emit or absorb heat at the junctions of a circuit consisting of two different conductors. In the latter case, a cooling effect occurs which has very recently found interesting applications (*see* p. 121).

It is quite simple to calculate the thermal efficiency η of such a cooling process. In the stationary state a thermo-electric potential difference arises which corresponds to the temperature difference produced by the external current by means of the Peltier effect. Its value $U_{th} = \alpha T$ is proportional to the temperature. The temperature difference caused by the external current will also produce a heat flow amounting to $\kappa \Delta T$ (where κ is the thermal conductivity and ΔT the temperature difference). In the most favourable case (no losses), the output of heat will be equal to the input of electricity. If we denote the electrical conductivity by σ, we have

$$\kappa \Delta T = \alpha^2 \sigma T^2 \qquad \text{.... (3.6a)}$$

Since we are only interested in happenings at *one* of the junctions, we must multiply the right-hand side of equation 3.6a by $\frac{1}{2}$. This gives

$$\Delta T = \tfrac{1}{2} \frac{\alpha^2 \sigma}{\kappa} T^2 \qquad \text{.... (3.6b)}$$

By a simple transformation we get the thermal efficiency of the cooling process

$$\eta = \frac{\Delta T}{T} = \frac{\alpha^2}{2} \frac{1}{\left(\dfrac{\kappa}{\sigma T} \right)} \qquad \text{.... (3.6c)}$$

The thermal efficiency is therefore proportional to the square of the quantity α, the thermal e.m.f. (thermoelectric voltage per degree, which is a specific constant for each substance). In this last factor we recognize once more the expression from the Wiedemann–Franz–Lorenz law (equation 3.4a). It has the value C_{WFL} and is a physical constant. Since the efficiency depends on the square of the thermal e.m.f., the discovery of combinations of conductors with slightly higher thermal e.m.f.'s is sufficient to improve the efficiency of the cooling considerably. As is shown below, this fact is extremely important for the industrial utilization of the Peltier effect (cf. p. 121).

Since, for reasons of energy conservation, the thermal efficiency cannot be greater than 1, it follows from equation 3.6c that there is an upper limit to the thermal e.m.f. (α_g), namely

$$\alpha_g = \sqrt{\left(2\;\frac{\kappa}{\sigma T}\right)} \qquad \ldots (3.6d)$$

The significance of this will be discussed later (cf. p. 115).

Our theory can also be used to explain induction, i.e. the production of an electromotive force by the movement of a conductor in a magnetic field. For this purpose, we may imagine a piece of a conductor as a vessel containing an electron gas (*Figure 4*). We move this vessel through a transverse magnetic field, and observe that the individual electrons,

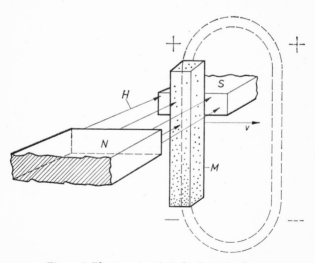

Figure 4. Electromagnetic induction of voltage

which, as a result of this motion, form a current, are deflected to one side by the transverse magnetic field. In *Figure 4* the directions have been chosen in such a way that this deflection is downwards, but this means that the lower end of the conductor is negatively charged with respect to the upper end. This explains the appearance of an induced potential difference. To induce a current, the conductor must be connected to form a circuit, taking care that the second part of the circuit does not move through the magnetic field too, because this would induce an equal potential difference which would cancel out the first so that no induced current could flow. But if the second arm of the circuit is arranged to be outside the magnetic field, so that when the first arm of the circuit moves the magnetic flux alters, then the induced potential difference between the two parts of the conductor will start an induced current. A potential difference will therefore be induced between the ends of an open conductor when it merely intersects lines of force, but a current can only be induced by a change in the magnetic flux through a circuit formed by a closed conductor.

The hypothesis of an electron gas also explains the emission effects, of which the thermionic and photoelectric are the best known. The electrons moving quasi-freely in the metal cannot simply leave the crystal lattice, in which they are in a state of electrical equilibrium. They have to do work against the forces of attraction, because for each electron emitted, the crystal lattice acquires a positive unit of charge. The energy for this work must come to the electrons from outside. The different emission effects differ in the way in which this energy is introduced.

For example, it may be heat energy, obtained by heating the electron gas. This gives the individual electrons high kinetic energies, which enable them to overcome the potential 'barrier' and perform the work necessary to leave the crystal. They will continue to leave until the positive charge on the crystal is sufficient to prevent any more electrons leaving. Those which have already left form a negatively charged space cloud above the emitting surface. In some experimental arrangements the electrons are drawn off by electrodes, thus enabling a continuous flow to take place (*Figure 5a*). We can therefore imagine the thermionic emission of electrons from metal surfaces as a process of evaporation. The relation between the density of the thermionic current of electrons and the temperature can be deduced by means of the thermodynamic Clausius–Clapeyron equation, and is known as Richardson's equation:

$$i = AT^2 e^{-\frac{\Phi}{kT}} \qquad \dots (3.7a)$$

Here i denotes the density of the thermionic current of electrons, A is a physical constant, which Schottky found to have the value 60·2 A cm^{-2} deg.$^{-2}$ for tungsten, T is the absolute temperature, k is Boltzmann's constant (*see* p. 14)

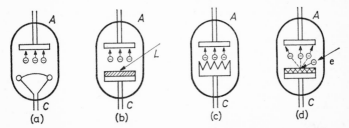

Figure 5. Liberation of free electrons: (a) Emission from glowing cathode; (b) Photoelectric emission; (c) Emission in a field; (d) Secondary emission. (A—anode, C—cathode, e—incident electron)

and $\Phi = eU$ is the work of emission, depending on the electrons and the material of the cathode. This can vary within wide limits with the state of the surface of the cathode.

The Clausius–Clapeyron equation for the evaporation process can be obtained as follows. If a liquid of volume V_2 receives a heat of vaporization E, then a fraction $E.\eta$ (where $\eta = \Delta T/T$ is the thermal efficiency) of this heat will be used in turning the liquid into vapour (gas) and changing its volume into the volume V_1 of this gas at a pressure Δp, where $V_2 \ll V_1$. This work of expansion is given by

$\Delta p\,(V_1 - V_2)$. We may therefore write:

$$\Delta p\,(V_1 - V_2) = E\Delta T/T \qquad \ldots\,(3.7b)$$

This gives the differential equation

$$T\frac{dp}{dT}(V_1 - V_2) = E \qquad \ldots\,(3.7c)$$

This is the Clausius–Clapeyron equation. Since it has been assumed that V_2 is negligible compared with V_1, and that the equation of state for gases can be applied to the volume V_1, then $V_1 = RT/p$ can be put in equation 3.7c to get

$$\frac{1}{p}\frac{dp}{dT} = \frac{d\ln p}{dT} = \frac{E}{RT^2} \qquad \ldots\,(3.7d)$$

Integrating, and remembering that the gas pressures p_1 and p_2 behave in the same way as the concentrations n_1 and n_2, we have

$$\ln n_1/n_2 = \ln p_1/p_2 = +\frac{E}{RT} = +\frac{NeU}{NkT} \qquad \ldots\,(3.7e)$$

or, putting $eU = \Phi$

$$n_2 = n_1\,e^{-\frac{\Phi}{kT}} \qquad \ldots\,(3.7f)$$

which we have already come across under the name of the Boltzmann distribution function (equation 3.5f) and deduced when discussing the diffusion of electrons by means of Einstein's law (equation 3.3a) (cf. p. 15). For the thermal current of electrons (current density i) the number z of the electrons leaving the cathode per unit time is the deciding factor: $i = \bar{a}z$ ($\bar{a}$ is the factor of proportionality). In the stationary state this is equal to the number of electrons returning to the cathode, and this again is proportional to the concentration n_2 in the outside space and to the velocity of the electrons (proportionality factor a). Since the kinetic energy is proportional to the temperature, so that the velocity is proportional to $\sqrt{T}$, we may write:

$$i = \bar{a}z = an_2\sqrt{T} = an_1\sqrt{T}\,e^{-\frac{\Phi}{kT}} \qquad \ldots\,(3.7g)$$

THEORY OF ELECTRICAL CONDUCTION

Comparison shows that this is Richardson's equation 3.7a, except that it has the factor $\sqrt{T}$ instead of T^2 before the exponential term. The theoretical reason for this lies in the Boltzmann distribution of the energies of the electrons, which is implicit in the vaporization equation. We have already found, when calculating the contact potentials, that this led to a result differing from the experimental value. Here again a modification of the theory, discussed below (*see* p. 31 ff.), leads to the result given in equation 3.7a.

The energy required to do the work necessary to leave the metal can also be obtained from electromagnetic radiation (light). Einstein's quantum theory of light states that, although light has for long been regarded as a typical wave phenomenon, under certain circumstances it seems to have a corpuscular nature too. Einstein, following Planck, associated a light corpuscle (or quantum of light, $h\nu$) with a quantity of energy E proportional to the frequency of the radiation (ν) (cf. equation 2.2a). From Lenard's studies of light and electricity, Einstein concluded that the elementary interaction between light and electricity is always the transfer of the energy of one quantum of light to exactly one electron. This enables us to state the balance of energy in the interaction between light and electrons:

$$h\nu = \tfrac{1}{2}mv^2 + \varphi \qquad \ldots . (3.8a)$$

In this equation $\tfrac{1}{2}mv^2$ is the energy of motion of the free electron after leaving the surface of the metal and φ is the work of emission, including the energies required by the electron both to reach the surface, and to cross it. If once more we put $\tfrac{1}{2}mv^2 = eU$, that is to say, if the kinetic energy is measured in 'electron volts', equation 3.8a can be written in the form:

$$h(\nu - \nu_0) = eU \qquad \ldots . (3.8b)$$

in which we have put $eU_0 = h\nu_0$, so as to express the fact that $h\nu_0$ is the minimum energy needed to leave the metal. Equation 3.8b gives this energy for $U = 0$, i.e. an electromagnetic radiation of frequency ν_0 or wave-length $\lambda_0 = c/\nu_0$ (where λ_0 is the photoelectric threshold wave-length) which is just sufficient to enable an electron to leave the surface (with a velocity $v = 0$) (*Figure 5b*).

There is also an effect, known as the 'field effect' or cold electron emission, in which a strong electrostatic field liberates electrons. It takes place at electrodes having considerable curvature (points), because there the field strength can reach values of 10^6 V/cm, which are sufficient to pull electrons out of the atomic bond, for which the accelerating voltage need only be of the order of 10^3 V (*Figure 5c*). Finally, among the emission effects must be mentioned the emission of secondary electrons, in which the energy required to enable the electrons to leave the metal is imparted by mechanical collisions. The cathode is bombarded with either ions or electrons. An ionic bombardment takes place in a gas discharge, when fresh bombarding particles (ions) are continually formed by collisions between the electrons liberated and the gas molecules (gas atoms) (collision ionization). Owing to the way the thermal energies are distributed, there are always sufficient collisions taking place between very fast molecules of gas to produce some ions, and when a voltage is applied to the cathode these ions hit the cathode and liberate the first electrons by their impact, and the discharge begins. The number of positively and negatively charged particles then increases by a chain reaction, and is limited only by the resistance of the current circuit and the current-producing capacity of the voltage source.

The behaviour of the cathodes when bombarded with electrons depends very much on the state of their surface. The bombarding electrons, generally photoelectric or thermionic in origin, usually liberate more than one secondary electron each, when the accelerating voltages are several hundred volts. The ratio of the number of bombarding electrons to the number of secondary electrons released is called the coefficient of secondary emission δ. Surface layers of caesium oxide on silver ($\delta = 7$) and magnesium oxide on magnesium ($\delta = 18$) have particularly high values of δ. Such cathodes are often used to amplify weak photoelectric effects, in secondary-electron multipliers, or photomulti-

THEORY OF ELECTRICAL CONDUCTION

pliers. Unfortunately the energy balance for the simple process of secondary emission cannot be given in a form corresponding to the Einstein equation (3.8a). *Figure 5d* is a diagram of an experimental arrangement for liberating secondary electrons.

In the explanation of the phenomenon of contact potential (p. 22) and in the deduction of Richardson's equation (p. 29) it was found that the experimental results did not agree with the results of our theory, otherwise so successful, of the electronic nature of the electrical behaviour of metals. There is another aspect from which our working hypothesis of observed phenomena is incorrect. The way in which we equated the thermal behaviour of atoms and electrons, implicitly assuming that the Boltzmann distribution which has proved applicable to the theory of heat (equations 3.5f and 3.7f) also holds good for the energies of electrons in metals, would require the electrons to make a considerable contribution to the specific heat—about 50 per cent—because if the Boltzmann distribution of energy holds good there are as many electrons as atoms in the metal able to receive heat energy. But no such proportion has ever been observed. It could not have escaped observation, for it would have been evinced, for example, by magnetic and electric fields having an influence on the specific heat. The explanation for this behaviour of the electron gas was first found when Sommerfeld applied Fermi statistics to it instead of the Boltzmann energy distribution. The Fermi statistics differ from those of Boltzmann in that not all particles can assume all the energy values, but only two electrons can possess a given value of energy, which is then occupied and not available for any of the other electrons. The low energy values, in particular, will be very quickly occupied at low temperatures in this way. Since the electrons, owing to their very small mass, can only absorb very small quantities of energy, the energy states are filled by them up to temperatures of 50,000 deg. This means that within this range the electron gas does not behave like a normal gas, but behaves degenerately. It can only receive as much energy as it simultaneously loses, so that there can only be an interchange of the energy carriers, a change of place in

31

the occupied energy states—in our case the electrons—but no change in the internal energy (increase in specific heat from the electronic fraction) can occur. It is thus only possible for the electrons to participate in the conduction of heat when the electron gas is degenerate. Sommerfeld's theory results in the electron gas contributing only 0·5 per cent to the specific heat at normal temperatures ($T = 300°$ K); but such a small fraction is within the limits of errors of measurement of the specific heat. Sommerfeld's modification of the electron gas theory helps it to win recognition as a valid theory of electronic conduction and the electrical behaviour of metals. In semiconductors, whose concentration of electrons will usually be at least 10,000 times less than that in metals, the electron gas will only have all its energy states filled up to energies corresponding to temperatures 10,000 times lower than the temperature at which the electron gas in metals degenerates. The electron gas in semiconductors is therefore not degenerate in the normal temperature range, and its behaviour can be described by the Boltzmann energy distribution.

The exponential function characteristic of the Boltzmann distribution (equation 3.5f) occurs in a different form in the Fermi distribution. For the concentration of a degenerate electron gas n_M in a metal or a highly-doped semiconductor (*see* p. 55) we have:

$$n_M = \text{const.} \frac{1}{e^{E-E_0/kT} + 1} \approx \text{const. } e^{-(E-E_0)/kT} \quad \dots (3.9a)$$

so long as $E \gg E_0$, so that the summand 1 can be neglected in comparison with the exponential function in the denominator. In the exponent, the value of the energy will be less than that in the Boltzmann distribution by an amount E_0. [E_0 represents the maximum value of energy up to which the energy states are fully occupied (Fermi level)].

The participation by the charged particles in the thermal vibrations, which can only be understood statistically, results in the current of charged particles being also subject to statistical fluctuations. By suitable amplification (10^8 times) these can be acoustically demonstrated as a noise (thermal noise). This shows the corpuscular nature of the electric current, whereas down to this limit it is possible to imagine it as continuous.

Nyquist deduced, on thermodynamic grounds, that the noise output N_s is

$$N_s = 4kT\Delta\nu \qquad \dots(3.9b)$$

where $\Delta\nu$ is the range of frequencies (bandwidth) for which this output is to be determined. Equation 3.9b leads to the following equations for the noise voltage U_s and current I_s:

$$U_s = \sqrt{4kTR\Delta\nu} \qquad \dots(3.9c)$$

and

$$I_s = \sqrt{\frac{4kT}{R}\Delta\nu} \qquad \dots(3.9d)$$

Table 2 gives, as an example, values of the noise voltage U_s for various values of resistance when $\Delta\nu = 10,000$ c/s, $T = 300°$ K, i.e. a noise output of $N_s = 1 \cdot 6.10^{-16}$ W.

Table 2. Resistance Noise (Noise Output $N_s = 1 \cdot 6.10^{-16}$ W)

	R (ohms)					
	10	10^2	10^3	10^4	10^5	10^6
U_s (μV)	0·04	0·13	0·40	1·26	4·00	12·60

When we considered the reasons for the electrical properties of metals, we started by assuming that between the state in which the valence electron is bound to the atom, and that in which it leads a quasi-free existence as a conduction electron, the transition is continuous. One of the reasons for this assumption was that the lattice potential almost counteracts the force of attraction between the atom and its outermost valence electron, and another was that the thermal energy at normal temperatures ($T = 300°$ K) is already enough to wipe out the difference between the bonded and free states.

The difference between the conduction of electricity in semiconductors and in metals does not, however, lie only in the difference in the behaviour of the electron gas, discussed above, but also in the fact that there is no continuous transition between the bonded and free states of the valence electron, such as we have assumed to exist in metals. This can be best made clear by means of an example. Take, as a typical example of a semiconductor, the element germanium (Ge). The crystal structure of germanium—as also of silicon and some of the $A^{III}B^{V}$ compounds—resembles the lattice of diamond. The diamond lattice consists of tetrahedra fitted together in such a way that each point of the lattice is equidistant from four nearest neighbouring points (*Figure 6a*).

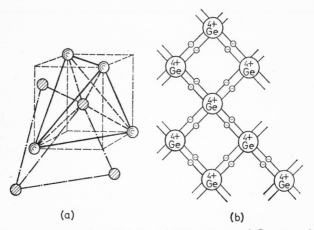

(a)   (b)

Figure 6. Diamond-type lattice: (a) Arrangement of Ge *atoms in a crystal; (b) Two-dimensional diagram of (a)*

The lattice is held together by homopolar or covalent bonds. One of the four valence electrons of a germanium atom interacts with one of the valence electrons of one of the four neighbouring atoms. The resultant bonding forces, called exchange forces, which can only be explained by the theory of wave mechanics (*see* p. 40 ff.), can be considered as if the valence electrons which interact belonged alternately to first one and then the other Ge atom, so that the relation between neighbouring atoms will be similar to that between two children playing ball with each other, using two balls (*Figure 6b*).

At normal temperatures ($T = 300°$ K) the strength of this double bond will be somewhat weakened by thermal energy, but not so much as is the case with metals. A few electrons, as a result of the Boltzmann distribution of thermal energies, may well be able to move about the lattice quasi-freely; but for the conductivity to reach any appreciable value, more energy must be applied to loosen these double bonds.

This energy can come from heating, for example, or it may arise from the incorporation of small quantities of impurity elements in the crystal lattice of the semiconductor— in this case, germanium. This causes imperfections in the lattice, so that these impurity atoms are called centres of imperfection. For example, the incorporation of impurity atoms which have one more valence electron than Ge means that this excess electron is only very lightly bonded in the lattice. It can therefore be rendered quasi-free merely by the heat of the surroundings, and will then be available for conduction of electricity. Elements which have more than four valence electrons and are thus suitable for incorporation in the lattice of, say, Ge, are phosphorus (P), arsenic (As), and

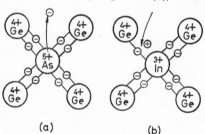

(a)   (b)

Figure 7. Impurity conduction: (a) Donor (electron); (b) Acceptor (defect electron, positive hole)

antimony (Sb). They are called electron donors and are said to produce *n*-type conduction (*Figure 7a*)—because the electrons to which they give rise are negatively-charged particles. On the other hand, it is also possible to add elements possessing only three valence electrons (electron capturers, acceptors). These include boron (B), aluminium (Al), gallium (Ga), and indium (In), for example. The imperfections which these atoms cause in the crystal lattice consist of the absence of one electron from the bond. The imperfection tries to capture an electron to complete its bond. This electron has to come from another bond which was previously complete. When it migrates, it will leave behind an excess positive charge of one elementary unit. We may say that the absence of the bonding electron leaves behind a positive hole. If an electron is recaptured, however, then a positive hole will arise at some other point in the crystal. In this way this absence of an electron, known as a defect electron, or more usually as a hole, moves through the crystal as a positive hole, resulting in the conduction of electricity just as if it were a positively charged particle (*Figure 7b*). This is called *p*-type conduction. This 'hole conduction' can be very easily demonstrated by the analogy of a row of occupied seats, in the middle of which there is one seat free (hole); by individual persons (electrons) moving along, the empty place (hole) moves to the edge—this corresponds to the process whereby defect electrons are responsible for conduction in semiconductors. We have said all this because with semiconductors we have to distinguish between different kinds of conduction processes. First, we have 'intrinsic conduction'. This is the conduction in the pure substance. It is caused by those of its electrons which have enough thermal energy to be able to leave the double bond and exist as quasi-free electrons. Holes left by the freeing of these electrons only play a part for recombination and pair formation. As has been made clear, the concentration of the electrons participating in intrinsic conduction will be much lower than that of the electron gas in metals. The concentration of the electrons responsible for intrinsic conduction will be denoted by n_i throughout. In the second place, we have extrinsic conduction. This consists of either electron conduction (*n*-conduction), in which more quasi-free electrons are made available by the incorporation in the crystal lattice of impurity atoms with excess valence electrons, or in hole conduction (*p*-conduction) resulting from the incorporation of impurity atoms which have fewer valence electrons than the atoms of which the lattice consists.

If the concentration of electrons in n-conduction is denoted by n_- and that in p-conduction by n_+, then in thermal equilibrium we have the following relation between these two quantities and the concentration of electrons responsible for intrinsic conduction:

$$n_- . n_+ = n_i^2 \qquad \ldots . (3.10a)$$

The first conclusion drawn from this equation is that the excess of charge carriers of one type (majority carriers) over those of the other type (minority carriers) always determines the nature of the conduction in the basis element (doped) with its donor *and* acceptor impurities; and the second is the interesting fact that the product of the concentrations of electrons and of holes depends neither on the concentration of the impurity atoms nor on the energy conditions.

In order to deduce equation 3.10a we need to go more closely into the manner in which electrons are made available. The different processes of conduction have this in common: in each, pairs of charges are formed by thermal means. The most loosely bonded valence electron is, by the heat energy given to it, enabled to break away from the atom and to leave it behind as a positively charged ion. In recombination, the opposite process takes place, and in thermal equilibrium the two processes balance each other out. The probability of recombination is proportional to the product of the concentrations of the recombining partners. Pair formation, on the other hand, is governed by a Boltzmann distribution (cf. equations 3.5f and 3.7f), so that it is essentially a function of temperature, but in thermal equilibrium ($T = \text{const.}$) it will have a constant value. for thermal equilibrium, therefore,

$$n_- . n_+ = \text{const.} \qquad \ldots . (3.10b)$$

If the impurity conduction be removed ($n_- = n_+$), only the intrinsic conduction of the semiconductor remains. From this it follows that the constant must have the value n_i^2, which gives equation 3.10a.

SEMICONDUCTORS

Pair formation, being a process generated thermally, is governed by the Boltzmann distribution (equation 3.5f). If n_z indicates the number of pairs formed per unit volume, we have

$$n_z = C^2 e^{-\Delta E/kT} \qquad \ldots\ldots (3.10c)$$

But the number of pairs n_z is proportional to the concentration of either partner—and therefore to n_i^2—from equation 3.10a. From equation 3.10a, therefore, we have:

$$n_- = C e^{-\Delta E/2kT} \qquad \ldots\ldots (3.10d)$$

$$n_+ = C e^{-\Delta E/2kT} \qquad \ldots\ldots (3.10e)$$

$$n_i = C e^{-\Delta E/2kT} \qquad \ldots\ldots (3.10f)$$

in which C is a factor of proportionality depending on the concentrations n_0 of the atoms in the lattice and n_D or n_A of the donors or acceptors, as well as on the probabilities W_0, W_D, and W_A of recombination in pair formation:

$$C = W_0 n_0 = \sqrt{\frac{n_D n_A}{W_D W_A}} \qquad \ldots\ldots (3.10g)$$

Imperfections arising by pair formation within the lattice are often known as 'Frenkel defects' after their discoverer. Lattice vacancies at the surface, which are filled proportional to n_0 in accordance with the Boltzmann distribution (equation 3.5f) ($C^2 = n_0$), are called 'Schottky defects'. These latter, in particular, play a part in boundary layers (*see* the deduction of Shockley's equation, p. 58).

Frenkel defects in semiconductors can be produced by irradiation with neutrons or γ-rays in order to influence the intrinsic conduction.

As Frenkel showed, thermal excitation will not necessarily completely liberate an electron from the positively charged residue of the atom (hole), but it may leave the electron still partly bound to it. These excited states of a combination of electron and positive hole (which are overall neutral and carry no charge) are called excitons. They may be used to explain optical absorption in which no photoelectric effect is observed.

It has also been found that in ionic crystals electrons and holes can polarize their immediate surroundings. This state of polarization moves with the carriers of charge which produce it, which are therefore called polarons. They reduce the potential energy of the crystal lattice and lower the energy level of the carriers belonging to the polaron by some tenths of an electron volt.

As has already been shown, the difference between electronic conduction in metals and in semiconductors consists in the fact that in semiconductors a certain amount of energy is needed to free the conduction electrons, or, in other words, an energy threshold must be crossed; this arises from the fact that a certain amount of work is needed to break the bond between the atoms in the crystal lattice. Different semi-conductors differ in the amount of this threshold energy. If this quantity of energy required to separate charged particles is very high, the conductivity will fall below the figure pre-viously given as the lower limit for semiconductors, and we speak no longer of a semiconductor, but of an insulator. From this it follows that the differences between semi-conductors and insulators are only gradual, and depend on the magnitude of the threshold energy. This energy region is generally called the forbidden zone; conduction electrons are unable to exist in it. In metals, the energy regions of the conduction and valence electrons overlap (cf. p. 48), and there is no forbidden zone.

The following, more detailed, treatment will make the idea of a forbidden zone more plausible and understandable; for the existence of the different zones of permitted and forbidden energies can be more easily explained by the wave theory of the electron (*see* p. 43), of which more knowledge than is given here is needed. But the treatment so far has shown that the observed phenomena can also be explained with the aid of the corpuscular model with a fair degree of satisfaction.

4

THE BAND MODEL OF THE ELECTRONS

IT HAS already been explained that a wave-length λ_e can also be associated with the electron (cf. equation 2.3), but the physical meaning of the amplitude of vibration Ψ of this wave has not as yet been made clear. The many attempts to evolve an apparently unitary hypothesis have been foiled *a priori* by the impossibility of combining the two ways of thinking—the particle and wave theories—which are based on contradictory assumptions. It has not therefore been possible to give an altogether satisfactory and obvious meaning to the amplitude function of a wave of matter. There was at first, indeed, an attempt to define a density of electric charge by means of the square of the amplitude of vibration, so as to connect the wave hypothesis with the particle hypothesis in such a way that the wave packets of neighbouring frequencies, formed by the overlapping of waves, could be identified with the particles, but it had to be recognized that the concept of such wave packets breaks down as soon as we try to make them transport a finite amount of energy. Born's statistical hypothesis was always more satisfactory and is now preferred. It considers the amplitude function $\Psi(x, y, z, t)$ as a measure of the probability that the particle which corresponds to the wave will be found in the place (x, y, z) at time t.

The amplitude function $\Psi(x, y, z, t)$ must, of course, satisfy a partial differential equation of the second order, as do all wave functions formally. For simplicity, we shall consider a wave spreading in one dimension, the x-direction, and write the differential equation:

$$\frac{\partial^2 \Psi}{\partial t^2} = w^2 \frac{\partial^2 \Psi}{\partial x^2} \qquad \ldots (4.1a)$$

where the constant w has the dimensions of a velocity: as appears from consideration of the solutions of the differential equation, this is the phase velocity with which the wave moves forwards. From the viewpoint of electron theory, the local behaviour of the wave function Ψ is of greatest interest. We shall therefore put the differential equation 4.1a into a form which is independent of time, in which we make a certain assumption about its variation with time, namely, that it is a harmonic function. With this assumption, we can write for Ψ:

$$\Psi(x, t) = \psi(x) e^{-i2\pi\nu t} \qquad \ldots (4.1b)$$

Inserting this in equation 4.1a, we get:

$$\frac{d^2\psi}{dx^2} + 4\pi^2 \frac{\nu^2}{w^2} \psi = 0 \qquad \ldots (4.1c)$$

Between the wave-length λ, the frequency ν and the phase velocity w there is always the relation $\lambda = w/\nu$. Substituting from equation 2.2b, we therefore have now:

$$\left(\frac{\nu}{w}\right)^2 = \left(\frac{mv}{h}\right)^2 = \frac{2m(E-U)}{h^2} \qquad \ldots (4.1d)$$

where E is the total energy and U the potential energy, so that the difference $(E-U) = T$ represents the kinetic energy. Substituting in equation 4.1c from 4.1d, we get Schrödinger's equation, 4.1e, in the form independent of time.

The amplitude fuction of a wave spreading in one dimension only varies with distance in a way given by solving the time-independent Schrödinger equation (4.1e):

$$\frac{d^2\psi}{dx^2} + \frac{8\pi^2 m}{h^2}(E-U)\psi = 0 \qquad \ldots (4.1e)$$

SEMICONDUCTORS

This equation is called after Schrödinger, who in 1926 succeeded in giving differential equations for the vibrations of matter waves in atoms, and in deducing from them the axioms of Bohr's theory of the atom.

Since we have eliminated the dependence on time, and are considering one dimension only, equation 4.1e is a total differential equation of the second order, and it is easily seen that it will only have periodic solutions for positive values of the factors preceding the function, and otherwise it only has solutions which die away rapidly. For constant values of the potential energy U the sign of this factor depends on the value of the total energy E. The values of E for which equation 4.1e has periodic solutions are therefore called the characteristic values or eigen-values of this differential equation, and the functions $\psi(x)$ which are found to be the solutions of the equation are called its eigen-functions.

The solutions will undoubtedly be very different if the potential energy is no longer considered to be constant, but a function of distance. This will be the case, for example, when an electron moves in the periodic potential field of a crystal lattice, as in the process of electronic conductivity. The value of the potential energy U will then fluctuate about a constant value U_0 of the potential, with amplitude $f(x)$ whose value alters periodically with the lattice constant a so that, e.g., $f(x+a) = f(x)$.

The Schrödinger equation for the motion of an electron in a crystal lattice extending in one direction only will then have the form:

$$\frac{d^2\psi}{dx^2} + \frac{8\pi^2 m_e}{h^2}(E - U_0 - f(x))\psi = 0 \qquad \dots (4.2a)$$

Although E, in equation 4.1e, is able to assume a continuous series of positive values, then, so long as $E > U$ and U is constant, this is certainly not the case with the eigen-value E in equation 4.2a. The value $(U_0 + f(x))$ is periodically exceeded, and the series of eigen-values is broken up into a series of bands, narrow for small values of E and growing wider as E increases. Between these bands of permitted energies, for which the differential equation 4.2a possesses

BAND MODEL OF THE ELECTRONS

periodic solutions, i.e. for energy regions in which electron waves can exist, there occur regions of forbidden energies—forbidden zones—i.e. regions for which equation 4.2a has no periodic solutions, and in which waves of matter cannot be propagated. This behaviour of the waves can be understood with the aid of *Figure 8*. Forbidden zones always occur when

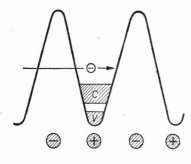

Figure 8. The regions where an electron can exist in the potential 'hill' of a crystal lattice (shown diagrammatically in one dimension) (C—conduction band; V—valence band)

the conditions for reflection at the potential walls fulfil Bragg's law of reflection, so that *standing* waves are formed. In this case, the electron corresponding to the wave will continue in a state of rest. This always occurs when the wave-length of the electrons is related to the lattice constant a by:

$$n\lambda_e = a \qquad \dots (4.2b)$$

where n is a whole number. When this treatment is extended to the case of a wave moving in three dimensions, it enables the diffraction of a material wave by a three-dimensional lattice of fixed points to be determined. Brillouin has carried out such calculations, assuming that the periodically-fluctuating portion $f(x, y, z)$ of the potential energy may be taken as small compared with U_0, and he arrived at a division of the energy space into forbidden and permitted regions, called Brillouin zones. For our purposes the above discussion should be sufficient to give an idea of how the features which are of importance for the theory of electronic conduction in semiconductors can also be derived from the simpler, one-dimensional case.

43

SEMICONDUCTORS

The energy regions represent only apparent continua, because they are formed by a very large number—about 10^{23} —cm^{-3} electron states. We are only interested in the two lowest bands of the band structure: the lowest valence band, which is filled with electrons and properly still belongs to the atom, and the next lowest, the conduction band, which is separated from the valence band by the widest forbidden zone. This band is only partially occupied: it contains only those electrons which have received sufficient energy to raise them into it across the forbidden zone. In the conduction band they are quasi-free and available for the purpose of conduction. The higher permitted regions, which are also largely unoccupied, are of no interest to us here, because of the high energies required to raise electrons into these bands. The band model which describes the processes of conduction in semiconductors is thus as shown in the diagram of *Figure 9.*

Figure 9. Electronic band model of a semiconductor with impurity conduction

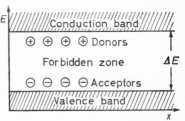

The different semiconductors differ in the width ΔE of the forbidden zone lying between the valence band and the conduction band. Table 4 (pp. 74–75) gives the values of ΔE for a series of semiconductors. The wider the forbidden zone, the lower will be the intrinsic conduction of the semiconductor; for it follows from the Boltzmann distribution law (equation 3.5f) that as ΔE increases the concentration of electrons in the higher conduction bands will decrease, so that fewer and fewer quasi-free electrons will be available for conduction. When $\Delta E \approx 3$ eV, therefore, the substance is no longer counted as a semiconductor but considered an insulator. It has already been stressed (p. 1) that this limit is to some extent arbitrary. For germanium, which has already been used several times as an example, we find the value 0·72 eV for the width of the forbidden zone, and for silicon, 1·12 eV (Table 4, pp. 74–75).

This ban on existence in the 'forbidden zones' applies only to electrons of the matrix element, but not to impurity centres, since these are formed by foreign atoms, which do not interrupt the regular crystal structure of the matrix, but whose presence causes interruptions in the periodic fluctuation of the lattice potential. In our electron band model, therefore, we must assume that the energy positions of these foreign atoms all lie in the forbidden zone. The behaviour already discussed (cf. p. 35) leads us to place the acceptors just above the valence band, while the donors will be near the upper limit of the forbidden zone, beneath the conduction band. On the energy scale, they are each (for the example of a germanium matrix) at a distance of approximately 0·02 eV from the two edges of the bands. Electrons supplied by the donors will therefore only have to provide this small amount of energy, while conduction electrons coming from the valence band need about 36 times as much energy—corresponding to the width of the forbidden zone. It may therefore be assumed on the one hand that all donors give up one electron to the conduction band, and, on the other hand, that all acceptors take one electron from the valence band and thereby cause a positive hole—an electron defect—to arise in the valence band. This assumption also agrees with the Boltzmann distribution law (equation 3.5f) which gives exponentially-increasing electron densities for decreasing values of ΔE.

Bloch arrived at corresponding results, starting from the wave number $k_e = 1/\lambda_e$ instead of the wave-length λ_e. The second of the equations (2.2b) can then be written:

$$J = \frac{h}{\lambda_e} = hk_e \qquad \dots (4.3a)$$

and, since $E = J^2/2m_e$, we get

$$E = \frac{h^2 k_e^2}{2m_e} \qquad \dots (4.3b)$$

SEMICONDUCTORS

Substituting in equation 2.2b from 4.3a, we get, for the velocity of translation v of the electron as a particle,

$$v = \frac{J}{m_e} = \frac{hk_e}{m_e} \qquad \dots (4.3c)$$

It can be deduced from equation 4.3b that for hk_e/m_e we may put dE/hdk_e, and equation 4.3c then becomes

$$v = \frac{1}{h} \frac{dE}{dk_e} \qquad \dots (4.3d)$$

From equation 4.3b it is seen that E varies with the square of the wave number k_e. Since the electron is at rest inside the forbidden zone—as already deduced (p. 43)—the velocity of the electron v must also have the value zero at the boundaries between the permitted and forbidden zones. It can therefore be concluded from equation 4.3d that at the zone boundaries:

$$\frac{dE}{dk_e} = 0 \qquad \dots (4.3e)$$

The same criterion applies to the position of the forbidden zones as in Brillouin's theory (equation 4.2b). If, instead of the wave-length, the wave number is inserted there, the position of the centre of gravity of the forbidden zone, about which the forbidden energy states are grouped, is given by:

$$k_e = \frac{n}{a} \qquad \dots (4.3f)$$

Thermal motion in the lattice helps to widen the energy bands as the energy increases. The fact that the atoms of the lattice are oscillating about their rest positions causes the potential 'hill' to vibrate. This changes the width of the potential 'valley'. This, again, causes the periodicity of the lattice to fluctuate, and therefore causes the lattice constants to fluctuate. According to equation 4.2b, or 4.3f, one would therefore expect to find a scatter in the values of the wave-lengths, or wave numbers k_e, about their averages.

The condition 4.3e for the zone boundaries means that the curve of energy versus wave number must have a horizontal tangent at these critical points, so that it behaves as shown in *Figure 10*.

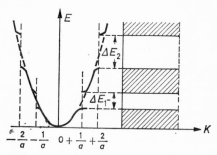

Figure 10. Behaviour of the energy as a function of the wave number for quasi-free electrons

With the Brillouin representation, we moved in a configuration space of which at least one coordinate can be understood directly as measuring extension in space, but the Bloch configuration space can no longer be related to physical reality as regards either of its two coordinates. This is the reason why this scheme of treatment—which is historically the older—has not been introduced until the end of our presentation of the interpretation of the behaviour of semiconductors. In this way we have avoided the difficulties which can easily arise on going back from a configuration space to a space-time presentation, which does represent reality, albeit incompletely.

We now have the following picture of the electrical behaviour of solids (*Figure 11*).

In metals, the valence band and the conduction band are either directly adjoining or overlapping (*Figure 11a* and *b*). The conduction band is not fully occupied and can therefore supply electrons for the conduction of electricity. The transition from the valence band to the conduction band requires so little energy that this can always be supplied by the thermal energy of the surroundings at normal temperatures $(T = 300°$ K).

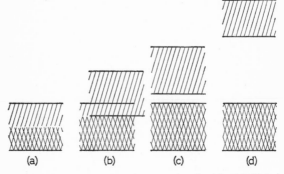

Figure 11. Arrangement of energy bands: (a) and (b) In a metal; (c) In a semiconductor; (d) In an insulator

In semiconductors, the valence band and conduction band are separated by a forbidden zone (*Figure 11c*), whose width may be anything up to a limit of $\Delta E \approx 3$ eV. The conduction band is only sparsely occupied, because only a few electrons have enough thermal energy to leap across the forbidden zone. These few electrons are responsible for the intrinsic conduction.

In insulators, the forbidden zone is wider than $\Delta E \approx 3$ eV, and an extraordinary quantity of energy would be required to cross this energy threshold (*Figure 11d*). The addition of this energy in the form of heat might destroy the crystalline structure. It is however possible to supply this energy electromagnetically (e.g. by light, x-rays, or alternating magnetic fields).

We have repeatedly said that the difference between semiconductors and insulators is only gradual, and the limit of energy $\Delta E \approx 3$ eV is more or less arbitrary (cf. p. 44). An ideal insulator would therefore be a substance whose forbidden zone was infinitely wide.

BAND MODEL OF THE ELECTRONS

Quite generally, the conduction of electricity may be said to take place only in unoccupied or partly occupied bands, and to be impossible in fully occupied bands (e.g., the valence band). In all processes of conduction in electronic semi-conductors, the particles which actually move are electrons, even in what is known as hole conduction. The introduction of the concept of 'positive hole', as a positive carrier of charge and as a symbol for the positive ion created by the transfer of an electron, does however simplify the treatment so much that this concept cannot but be helpful. But, in contrast to the quasi-free electron, the positive carrier of charge is confined to its position, because it is an ionized atom of the lattice. It is only the state of ionization caused by the transfer of the electron which migrates; externally, this is equivalent to the movement of a positive charge.

We shall now discuss an interesting relationship which can be deduced with the aid of equation 4.3d. From this the acceleration dv/dt can be deduced as:

$$\frac{dv}{dt} = \frac{1}{h} \frac{d}{dt} \left(\frac{dE}{dk_e} \right) = \frac{1}{h} \frac{d}{dk_e} \left(\frac{dE}{dt} \right) \qquad \ldots . (4.4a)$$

The differential quotient of energy with respect to time, i.e. the power, can however be expressed by the product of the effective force K and the velocity v. Once more taking 4.3d into account, we then have

$$\frac{dE}{dt} = Kv = K \frac{1}{h} \frac{dE}{dk_e} \qquad \ldots . (4.4b)$$

In conjunction with equation 4.4a, we therefore have an expression for the acceleration of an electron:

$$\frac{dv}{dt} = \frac{K}{m_e} = K \frac{1}{h^2} \frac{d^2E}{dk_e^2} \qquad \ldots . (4.4c)$$

This holds so long as equation 4.3a remains valid, i.e. as long as the energy E is a quadratic function of the wave number k_e. From 4.4c an expression for the mass of the electron can be arrived at in the following form:

$$(m_e)_{\text{eff}} = h^2 \left/ \frac{\mathrm{d}^2 E}{\mathrm{d}k_e^2} \right. \qquad \ldots (4.4\mathrm{d})$$

This definition of mass (4.4d) can also be retained in regions where its underlying assumptions no longer hold strictly, in order to be able to describe the behaviour of an electron in the potential 'hills' by analogy with its behaviour in a vacuum. We then speak of an effective mass, and the relation 4.3b no longer holds strictly. This is the case, for example, when E varies with k_e in the manner shown in *Figure 10*. The forbidden zone is then characterized $(\mathrm{d}E/\mathrm{d}k_e = 0)$ by the effective mass becoming infinitely large. But this only means that no force is able to move the electron in the forbidden zone, and that the velocity of the electron will there be $v = 0$. Since, by definition, the force K which we have employed in the definition of the effective mass was introduced as an external force acting on the electron, and may be overcome by stronger forces, under some circumstances, inside the lattice, it is possible that in certain regions the effective mass can even assume negative values. When using this concept, however, it is necessary to be quite clear from the outset that it is a useful but rather fictitious concept, introduced because with its aid the movement of electrons in a crystal can be described in a similar manner to the movement of electrons in a vacuum. The effective mass of an electron is identical with its true mass only so long as equation 4.3b can be assumed to be strictly true, i.e. when an electron moves without interruption in a vacuum and a quasi-free electron moves in the zones of permitted energy. The biggest deviations are found at the boundaries of the bands and in the forbidden zones (*see* equation 4.3e).

From equation 4.4d it follows that where the curve of E as a function of k_e shows strong curvature (i.e. for $\mathrm{d}^2 E/\mathrm{d}k_e^2 \gg 0$), the effective mass of the electrons, or holes, will be small, so that, from equation 3.3e, high mobilities would be expected (cf. Table 4, pp. 74–75).

BAND MODEL OF THE ELECTRONS

Electron-hole pair formation and recombination, which we have previously considered as a single-stage process between the valence and conduction bands, for intrinsic conduction, on the one hand, and between the impurity levels and both bands, for impurity conduction, can also proceed in two (or more) stages above this impurity level. Since this involves an impurity centre which, under certain circumstances, traps an electron which is on its way from the valence band to the conduction band, this process is called the trap process. A two-stage process was postulated as long ago as 1932 by Teichmann to explain the Dember crystal photoelectric effect (cf. p. 60). Two-stage processes have made possible the production of microwaves by means of semiconducting substances (cf. p. 124).

5

THE ELECTRICAL BEHAVIOUR OF JUNCTIONS

IF ADJOINING substances have different types of conduction, the different charge carriers will diffuse through the junction from both sides until a potential difference—the diffusion potential—is set up, which prevents any further exchange of charge (*see* p. 21). Such junctions are found between metals and semiconductors, and also between semiconductors having *p*- and *n*-conduction. Regions with *p*- and *n*-conduction may even adjoin within one and the same crystal of a semiconductor. The region near the junction (the transition region) will then become depleted in carriers of charge, because at first electrons from the *n*-conduction region will move into the *p*-conduction region, until the resulting potential difference prevents any more electrons crossing. The same applies to positive holes moving from the region of *p*-conduction to that of *n*-conduction. Most of the charge carriers which move into the junction recombine, thus reducing their concentration.

This depletion region has a high resistance (low conductance). It can be affected by an applied external field. If the direction of the field is such that the electrons or holes are drawn off to electrodes of opposite polarity, the depletion region becomes greater and the passage of current through it is very much impeded. If the field is reversed, however, electrons and holes are driven into the depleted region, so that it becomes narrower and electricity can pass through it more easily. Similar phenomena take place at the junction between a semiconductor and a metal in contact. In this case, the concentration of electrons in the metal ($\sim 10^{23}$ cm^{-3}) is much higher than in the semiconductor ($\sim 10^{18}$ cm^{-3}). An electric field forcing the electrons out of the metal into the semiconductor has an almost inexhaustible store to draw on.

If the field is in the opposite direction, however, only the few electrons in the conduction band of the semiconductor are available. The conductances will therefore be in about the same ratio as the electron concentrations, i.e. $1:10^5$. In this case also a threshold potential arises at the junction, in the form of the diffusion potential corresponding to the contact potential difference between the two substances (*see* p. 22). *Figure 12* illustrates these states of affairs for a semiconductor with *n–p*-conduction. *Figure 13* illustrates the phenomena at a junction between a metal and a semiconductor. In both cases the diagram is in terms of the band model of the electron.

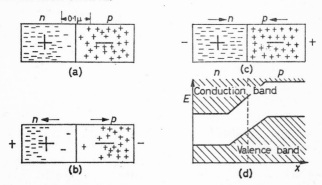

Figure 12. n–p-junction in a semiconductor: (a) Depletion region in the transition zone; (b) Growth of the depletion region in the reverse direction; (c) Shrinkage of the depletion region in the forward direction; (d) Electron band model of the transition region

The directional conduction of electricity at junctions between substances, arising from the different nature of their conductivities, is called unipolar conduction. It has technical applications in semiconductor rectifiers. The direction in which the combination of conductors has a high resistance is called the reverse direction, and that in which there is only a low resistance to the passage of electricity is called the forward direction.

As a small low-power component, the semiconductor rectifier is also known as a semiconductor diode, and diodes like this have another remarkable property: the reverse voltage has an upper limit. When the strength of the electric field produced in the junction by the reverse voltage is high enough to liberate electrons directly from the impurity centres

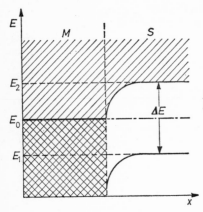

Figure 13. Junction between metal (M) and semiconductor (S)

or the atoms in the lattice (*see* p. 30), that is, to enable the valence electrons to gain the work required to raise them into the conduction band, we have the avalanche or Zener effect. The sudden appearance of a very large number of carriers of charge causes the collapse of the barrier, and the diode becomes permeable to electricity in the reverse direction. These Zener diodes are used in circuits in order to stabilize voltage. To use a hydrodynamic analogy, the Zener diode acts like an overspill. With high-power diodes (semiconductor rectifiers), not only does the Zener effect cause the junction to break down electrically, but the heat developed breaks down its structure too, for the quantities of heat released by the sudden rise in current cannot be removed quickly enough. Safety devices are therefore always found wherever semiconductor rectifiers are in service, to prevent overvoltages of the order of the Zener voltage.

Assuming that the depletion region between the regions of *n*- and *p*-conduction in a semiconductor is narrow compared with the mean free path of the diffusing charge carriers, i.e. that here recombination will be negligible, Shockley deduced a relation which very accurately describes the rectifying behaviour—unipolar conductance—of such junctions. It is:

$$i = i_s \left(e^{\frac{eU}{kT}} - 1\right) \qquad \ldots (5.1)$$

For negative values of the voltage U the exponential function will be negligible compared with unity, i.e. the current i will have the constant value i_s. This is the current in the reverse direction. For positive values of U, the exponential function predominates, and the current increases exponentially (*Figure 14a*). This is the typical characteristic of a rectifier.

In 1958 Esaki showed that semiconductor diodes have yet another peculiarity if they are very heavily doped with impurity atoms on both sides of the junction. In this way the concentration of the charge carriers can be allowed to become so high that the degenerate state is reached. Then, when a voltage is applied in the forward direction, the large supply of carriers made available by the heavy doping is exhausted first. Even at very low voltages the current increases rapidly until it reaches a maximum, then, as the voltage increases further, the current decreases again, until the normal diffusion and recombination current described above restore the exponential rise characteristic of rectifiers. Semiconductor diodes like this, heavily doped in a narrow region on both sides of the junction, therefore have a static characteristic like that shown in *Figure 14b*. Between the maximum (*A*) and the minimum (*B*), this curve has a downward tendency, i.e. in this range the diode has a negative resistance. It can therefore be used to produce oscillations if the working point is chosen on the falling portion of the characteristic.

We have explained the phenomena described by Zener and by Esaki with the aid of our corpuscular model of a semiconductor and of the impurity atoms embedded in its crystal structure. From the wave-theory viewpoint, the explanation of both these phenomena must be based on the wave-mechanical 'tunnel effect'. By this we understand the phenomenon of a low-energy wave of matter which can penetrate

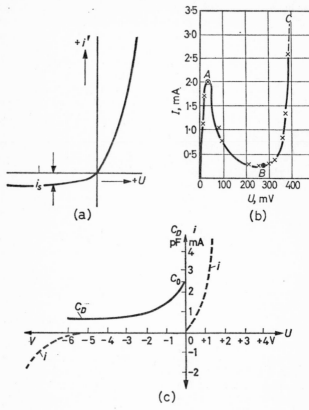

Figure 14. Behaviour of diodes: (a) Rectifier characteristic (after Shockley); (b) Characteristic of a tunnel diode; (c) Relation between capacitance and reverse voltage

threshold potentials of higher energy, and the narrower the potential 'hill', the more easily can the wave penetrate it. The particle theory cannot explain the phenomenon, for it states that a low-energy particle would be totally reflected by a

56

high-energy potential hill. But when a wave is totally reflected, part of the wave penetrates the potential hill with an amplitude which rapidly decreases exponentially. If the potential hill is narrow enough, the amplitude of this penetrating part of the wave will still be great enough for it to be able to appear behind the potential hill. According to our interpretation of the wave function Ψ (p. 40), this amplitude is a measure of the probability that the electron will appear behind the potential hill, if we confine our generalizations once more to the 'electron' particle. This electron, which, on the particle theory, could not possibly have reached the other side of the potential hill, has 'tunnelled through it', whence the name 'tunnel effect'. The probability of penetration in the wave-mechanical tunnel effect depends on the energy and the concentration of the particles represented by the wave, and on the width of the potential hill. In the phenomenon described by Esaki, when the diode has a falling characteristic in the forward direction, the high degenerate concentration of the charge carriers explains the existence of a considerable tunnel effect, and hence of the current maximum in *Figure 14b*. Diodes which are highly doped in a narrow region on both sides of the junction are therefore called tunnel diodes. In the case of the Zener effect, the probability of penetration by tunnelling is increased by the occurrence of high potentials at the junction, which raise the energy of the charge carriers towards the top of the potential hill. Since the displacement of the charge in the tunnel effect takes place almost at the speed of light ($c = 3.10^{10}$ cm/s), the tunnel diode can be used to produce oscillations of extremely high frequency ($\nu \geqslant 500$ Mc/s). Because the tunnel effect dies away more quickly than the thermal motion of the electrons ($v_{\text{therm}} \sim 10^5$ cm/s), tunnel diodes have extremely low noise (*see* p. 33).

A further phenomenon occurs at a junction, indicated by the fact that the capacitance of the junction in the reverse direction depends on the voltage (*Figure 14c*). This is explained by the fact that an imposed reverse voltage widens the depletion region. This process may be compared with the drawing together of the plates of a condenser to reduce its capacitance. The capacitance C_0 of the junction must therefore be a maximum for voltage $U = 0$ and decrease rapidly with rising reverse voltage. Shockley has given the following equation connecting the capacitance of the junction layer C_U at reverse voltage U and its maximum capacitance C_0:

$$C_U = \frac{C_0}{\sqrt{1 - \frac{5}{2}U}} \qquad \dots (5.2)$$

This property of semiconductor diodes has been found very valuable in connection with parametric amplification (*see* p. 127).

To deduce Shockley's equation (5.1), we need to go further into the diffusion process at the junction. Electrons diffuse out of the n-conducting layer into the p-conducting layer, and, vice versa, holes diffuse out of the p-conducting layer into the n-conducting layer. The concentrations of the two types of charge carriers will decrease in proportion as they penetrate deeper into the region of carriers of the opposite sign, to a final very low value which depends on the thermal equilibrium. Let us first consider the electrons, and let x be the coordinates along the path of diffusion, when we have for the electron current i_n:

$$i_n = ev\left[n\,(x) - n_p\right] \qquad \dots (5.3a)$$

where n_p is the value of the concentration of electrons in the region of p-conduction to which the concentration of the electrons diffusing into this region falls (*see* p. 52). Furthermore, $n\,(x)$ can be calculated from n_p, for there will be a rise in concentration along the path of diffusion caused by the applied external voltage U. We carry out the calculation in the same way as when deducing the Boltzmann distribution (equation 3.5c), and get:

$$n\,(x) = n_p\,e^{\frac{eU}{kT}} \qquad \dots (5.3b)$$

remembering that we must put $+\,dU$ in equation 3.5a instead of $-\,dU$, because in the present case U is not a negative (diffusion) potential (governed by the sign of the

ELECTRICAL BEHAVIOUR OF JUNCTIONS

electronic charge) but an external positive (penetration) potential.

Combining 5.3a and 5.3b, we get:

$$i_n = evn_p \, (e^{\frac{eU}{kT}} - 1) \qquad \dots (5.3c)$$

The same assumptions apply to the holes, so that a corresponding equation can immediately be deduced:

$$i_p = evp_n \, (e^{\frac{eU}{kT}} - 1) \qquad \dots (5.3d)$$

where i_p denotes the portion of the current due to the positive holes and p_n the concentration of holes in the n-conduction region. Combining 5.3c and 5.3d we get the total current i:

$$i = i_n + i_p = ev \, (n_p + p_n) \, (e^{\frac{eU}{kT}} - 1) \qquad \dots (5.3e)$$

If we now put:

$$i_s = v \, (n_p + p_n) \qquad \dots (5.3f)$$

we get the equation:

$$i = i_s \, (e^{\frac{eU}{kT}} - 1)$$

i.e. the Shockley equation as given in 5.1. The saturation value i_s for the reverse current arises from the production of charge carriers by thermal excitation, so that it is a function of temperature; but it is independent of the applied voltage, apart from the Zener effect which occurs at high reverse voltages (*see* p. 54).

The current density which can be carried by junctions of this sort without breaking down depends very largely on the material, for in rectifiers the drop in potential all occurs in the extremely narrow transition region, so that fields of the order of 500,000 V/cm can easily occur, and may be destructive. In constructing rectifiers, therefore, we attempt to make this junction wider by suitable doping with impurity atoms, i.e. by allowing the concentration of donors in the region of *p*-conduction to fall off slowly. In this way the following current-carrying capacities for various substances have been made possible, and are quite feasible technically.

Table 3. Current-Carrying Capacities of Junctions

	Substance			
	Cu₂O	Se	Ge	Si
j (A/cm²)	0·2	0·6	250	600

The high values achieved for Ge and Si are remarkable. They make possible the construction of rectifiers which take up very little space, the chief difficulty only being the removal of the considerable heat losses in the junction. The electrons in a semiconductor can also receive energy from elementary photon absorption instead of from an external field. This enables them to penetrate the junction in the reverse direction and diffuse backwards in the forward direction. The difference between the two drops in potential corresponds to the observed photo-e.m.f. This effect, which is directly connected with the existence of a junction, was described, almost at the same time, but quite independently, by Lange and Schottky in 1928. A diffusion potential produced photoelectrically was also observed for the first time in that year. In natural single crystals of semiconducting material (cuprous oxide), the decrease in the intensity of light resulting from optical absorption results in a decrease in concentration of electrons which is maintained by the energy of the light radiation, and consequently leads to a diffusion potential, as Dember and Teichmann have described. The photoelectric effect arising from the presence of a barrier layer has been given the name of barrier layer photoelectric effect, while the photoelectric effect arising from the irradiation of homogeneous material is called the crystal photoelectric effect (Dember effect). Both these effects can lead to the formation of an independent photo-e.m.f.

In the model of a *p–n*-junction, as in *Figure 12*, it may be supposed that the charge carriers formed photoelectrically, which are liberated near the junction, behave in such a way that the negative electrons which are formed in the zone of p-conduction migrate to the region of n-conduction, and the holes produced from the n-conduction zone migrate to the region of p-conduction. This interference with the balance of charge is compensated for, in the absence of external current, by an opposite potential at the end of the crystal, so that the distribution is as shown in *Figure 12b*. We have merely to suppose that the + or − sign at the ends of the crystal represents not an externally imposed voltage, but the sign of the barrier layer photo-e.m.f. The same applies to the description by means of the band model of the electron (cf. *Figure 13*). The photoelectric sensitivity of the semiconductor depends on the position in the spectrum of its optical absorption wave-lengths. For instance, the further the maximum of absorption lies towards the infra-red, the greater will be the photoelectric sensitivity of this semiconductor in this region of the spectrum. The barrier layer photoelectric effect is thus a maximum for cuprous oxide at $\lambda \sim 500$ mμ, and for p–n-conducting germanium at $\lambda \sim 1,400$ mμ.

The junction region—particularly the depletion region of a p–n-junction—can also be influenced by particles bombarding it from outside (β-rays, electrons, neutrons). The brief changes in conductance which result give rise to pulses of current which can be used to count the impinging particles. Semiconductor counters of this type are best when the junction lies close to the bombarded surface.

The crystal photoelectric effect, i.e. the occurrence of a photo-e.m.f., in semiconductors, can also be taken (following Teichmann) as an experimental proof that illumination can produce a junction. For, since the intensity of light decreases exponentially from the surface, there will be a corresponding decrease in the concentration of electrons, which is equivalent to a change in the nature of the conduction of the material (which originally had homogeneous conduction) (photoelectric barrier layer). The concept of the junction must now be extended, and we must think of it as having a thickness of not just a few microns, but perhaps of the order of cm. The same is true, as Welker has shown, of the effect of magnetism on the concentration of electrons in homogeneous semiconducting material. By placing such material in a magnetic field, junctions can be produced which act as magnetic barrier layers and make the semiconductor a unipolar conductor.

The need for at least two contacts between the metal leads and the semiconductor in order to form a current circuit means that there is a danger that we may get not only the effect of the junction between the p- and n-conducting regions of the semiconductor, which we want, but an unwanted effect as well, due to unipolar conducting junctions between the semiconductor and the metallic electrodes. The preparation of contact faces free from barrier layers is therefore very important. Since the directionality of the resistance is due to the differences in concentration of the charge carriers in the metal and in the semiconductor, contact faces can only be made free from barrier layers by making the density of the carriers in the regions immediately adjacent to the faces extremely high, so that when the current passes there will be an excess of carriers and no appreciable change in concentration will occur. This can be done by alloying the metallic contact adjacent to a p-conducting region of the semiconductor with a substance which acts as an acceptor, and doping with donors a metallic contact adjacent to an n-conduction region of the semiconductor. These impurity atoms will then diffuse into the adjacent layer of semiconductor, where they will produce a high concentration of carriers of p- or n-charge in a narrow region. At such a contact face, recombination and dissociation (pair formation) is very likely to take place between the electrons arising from conduction in the metal and holes from the region of p-conduction. No depletion region can therefore be formed there, and the resistance of the contact face will not be at all directional, i.e. there will be no barrier layer.

According to the band model of the electron, in the transition region between the metal and the semiconductor a state of equilibrium must be set up between the Fermi and Boltzmann distributions, i.e. from equations 3.9a and 3.5f we must have:

$$n_M = n_i, \quad \text{or} \quad e^{-\frac{E_2 - E_0}{kT}} = e^{-\frac{\Delta E}{2kT}} \qquad \dots (5.4a)$$

from whence it follows that:

$$E_0 = -\frac{\Delta E}{2} + E_2 \qquad \dots (5.4b)$$

where E_2 is the value of the energy at the lower edge of the conduction band. Equation 5.4b states that at the contact between a metal and a semiconductor with intrinsic conduction the Fermi level (see p. 32) runs through the middle of the forbidden zone (see Figure 13). When there is impurity conduction, the Fermi level will no longer be in this central position.

The possibility of multiplying the conductance of a semiconductor many times by various kinds of doping with acceptors and donors leads, as the next step, to the production of a semiconductor triode, i.e. a semiconducting crystal of which the first section, for example, is n-conducting, followed by a section of p-conduction, and finally another section of n-conduction. This somewhat resembles a combination of two n–p-rectifiers of the type in Figure 12a. This would not be of any particular interest if the effect were merely the sum of the effects of two opposing diodes. But if the middle region is made so narrow that the two junctions, at which barrier layers are formed as a result of charge carrier depletion, are pushed very closely together, then it becomes possible for charge carriers which have crossed from the first, n-conducting, section into the middle section to pass through this section, and through the second barrier layer, and exert electrical effects here and in the third section. For such an interaction to occur between the three sections of a semiconductor having different types of conduction, it is necessary for the thickness of the middle section to be less than the mean free path of the charge carriers. Then processes taking place in No. 1 depletion region can also extend and interact with those in No. 2 depletion region (*Figure 15a*). A semi-conductor triode of this sort is called a transistor. A transistor with a flat junction, as shown in *Figure 15* (in contrast to a point contact) is called a junction transistor, or, in the special case illustrated, an *n–p–n*-transistor. The point transistor (*Figure 15d*) is historically older; here the properties of the junction are restricted to the immediate surroundings of the points of contact between the two point electrodes, similar to the behaviour of the lead sulphide detector, which in the early days of radio played an important part as a rectifier of alternating high-frequency currents. Bardeen and Brattain discovered, in 1948, the special properties of the semiconductor triode, which we shall now discuss in more detail, in the form of a point-contact transistor.

It has become the custom to call the three electrodes which touch the semiconductor the emitter, the base and the collector (*Figure 15a–c*). When no current flows, the potential inside will be as shown in *Figure 15b* (on the band model). It is seen that there is a steep rise in potential at the first junction and a steep fall in potential at the second junction. Within

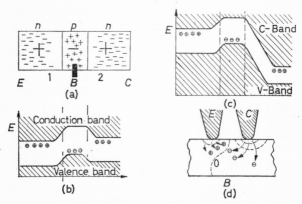

Figure 15. n–p–n-junction transistor: (a) Depletion region at the junctions; (b) Electron band model of the transistor; (c) Electron band model with applied voltage; (d) Paths of the carriers in the point transistor

64

the narrow region of *p*-conduction between the junctions, the potential is constant, i.e. here the charge carriers are not exposed to any electric field and move by thermal diffusion only. For this reason the middle layer—in our example the *p*-conducting layer—must be narrower than the mean free path. On the other hand, however, the mean free path can be made longer by reducing the number of recombinations in this region, that is, by doping the base region very lightly. If the mean free path $L \sim 1$ mm (for pure Ge), the thickness of the base region is chosen between 0·1 and 0·01 mm.

If a negative potential is applied to the emitter electrode and a positive potential to the collector electrode (both with respect to that of the base electrode), the electrons will leave the emitter region and pass through junction 1, diffuse through the base and influence the processes occurring at junction 2, i.e. control the flow of electrons between emitter and collector (*Figure 15a*). In particular, the electrons entering No. 1 depletion region from the emitter region will annul this state of depletion. Those electrons diffusing through the base zone which do not recombine with holes will annul No. 2 depletion layer, so that the resistance in the collector region is also reduced. But this means—as already mentioned—that the current of electrons flowing to the collector electrode is controlled. This behaviour of an *n–p–n*-transistor is shown in *Figure 15c* on the band model. The behaviour of the potential (the position of the edges of the bands) shows that the electrons diffusing through the base layer fall, as it were, into the positively biased collector region. Control of the collector current by means of the charge carriers from the emitter circuit generally results in amplification. It is mainly caused by a change in current in the emitter circuit, because the input resistance of this circuit is of the order of 100 Ω, which is low, so the control power is not negligible. In this way the semiconductor triode (transistor) behaves differently from the thermionic valve triode, which needs only a negligibly small control power for high values of the input resistance in the grid circuit ($\sim 10^4 \Omega$), the control being exerted mainly by a change in potential in the grid circuit. With this exception, Beneking has shown that there is a whole series of parallels between the modes of operation of semiconductor and vacuum triodes. In both cases, the operation depends on the possibility of influencing the movement of carriers of electricity. In the case of valves, the carriers are in the form of electrons supplied by emission from the cathode. The cathode must therefore be heated above the temperature of its surroundings in order that the electrons may overcome the relatively high potential necessary to leave the material of the cathode. In semiconductor transistors, the carriers in motion (electrons or holes) exist already, because the heat of the surroundings affords sufficient energy to enable them to lead a quasi-free existence. These are, primarily, the carriers obtained by doping with impurity atoms. The intrinsic conduction can be neglected (*see* p. 35). The emitter electrode may be considered as similar to the cathode of a valve. The collector electrode then corresponds to the anode, and the base to the grid. These analogies enable us to derive grounded circuits for transistors similar to those for valves. The grounded-cathode circuit of a valve corresponds to a grounded-emitter circuit for a transistor; the grounded-grid to a grounded-base; and the grounded-anode to a grounded-collector (*Figure 16a–c*). Analogies between the frequency behaviour, which is now discussed, are particularly interesting.

Valves are able to amplify and produce interference-free oscillations whose period is greater than the time taken for an electron to pass from grid to cathode. The reciprocal value of this period represents a critical frequency ν_{krR} up to which the valve is able to operate. If we denote by $\bar{v}$ the velocity of the electrons between cathode and grid, and by d the distance between grid and cathode, then we have for ν_{krR}:

$$\nu_{krR} = \frac{\bar{v}}{2d} \qquad \dots (5.5)$$

In the transistor, the charge carriers, as has already been seen (p. 65), move, in the base region which governs the control, as a result of their concentration gradient only (i.e. by diffusion). The mean velocity is therefore given by the concentration gradient. If it is assumed that a quantity of carriers of concentration n diffuse from the emitter side into the base

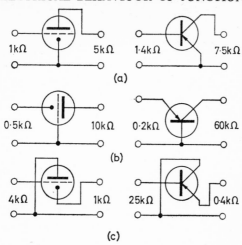

Figure 16. Grounded circuits of valves and transistors: (a) Grounded cathode/emitter connection; (b) Grounded grid/base connection; (c) Grounded anode/collector connection. (The resistances given correspond to those of valves EC92 and transistors OC12)

(after Beneking)

region, and, after passing through the base (of thickness d), are sucked off immediately they arrive at the collector side ($n_d = 0$), the concentration gradient will be n/d. If the charge carriers move with mean velocity $\bar{v}$, the current density will be $ne\bar{v}$, but it will also be equal to eDn/d, where D is the diffusion coefficient. For the mean velocity $\bar{v}$, therefore, we have:

$$\bar{v} = \frac{2D}{d} \qquad \dots . (5.6a)$$

The time taken to cross the base region of the transistor is $d/\bar{v}$, and the same considerations as given for valves, above, *show* that the transistor has a critical frequency v_{krT} given by:

$$v_{krT} = \frac{2D}{d^2} \qquad \dots . (5.6b)$$

67

This is the frequency up to which the transistor can operate properly.

Equations 5.5 and 5.6b both indicate what quantities must be adjusted in the manufacture of valves, or transistors, to make them suitable for very high frequency applications. We know that semiconductor triodes should have a thin base and a high diffusion coefficient, for very high frequencies. The mean velocities of electrons in a valve are of the order of 10^7 cm s^{-1}, but those of the charge carriers in a transistor, being pure thermal diffusion velocities, are about one-hundredth as high (10^5 cm s^{-1}). The first thing to do in attempting to make a transistor suitable for very high frequencies is therefore to increase the diffusion velocities. This can be done, for example, by utilizing an internal field effect in the base layer. For instance, in an n–p–n-transistor, the base may be doped with acceptors in such a way that there are more in the side towards the collector electrode, and there will then be a field within the base which accelerates the electrons flowing out of the emitter layer and increases their velocity. A transistor doped in this way is called a drift transitor. A doping up to the degenerated state causes very high velocities of the carriers of charge by the tunnel effect (tunnel transistor).

Multiple-layer transistors can also be made, corresponding to multiple-electrode valves. Here mention may be made of the n–p–n–p-transistor, whose construction resembles that of a pentode valve, and which is used particularly to produce relaxation oscillations and as a switching transistor (*see* p. 95). Moreover, it may be pointed out that the properties of the ordinary transistor already resemble those of a pentode. Since, in such a transistor, the field is zero in the base region, this means that the collector voltage does not extend to this region. As in a pentode, the collector current (corresponding to the anode current) is then largely independent of fluctuations in the collector (anode) voltage. This explains the characteristic of the grounded-base circuit, given elsewhere (*see Figure 33b*, p. 99).

The description of the electrical behaviour of junctions given in this chapter can be summed up in the statement that the anomalies in electrical conduction observed at junctions, particularly the dependence of conduction on the direction of the current, are always determined solely by differences in the concentration or the sign of the charge carriers between the two regions on each side of the junction, which have different types of conduction. A junction always represents a zone of transition between such regions.

F

6

THE PROPERTIES OF SEMICONDUCTING SUBSTANCES

OF THE typical semiconducting substances discussed in previous chapters, the one most frequently met is the element germanium (Ge), but the element silicon (Si) and the materials known as $A^{III}B^V$ compounds have also been mentioned. Other important semiconductors are the elements selenium (Se), tellurium (Te), bismuth (Bi) and their compounds and alloys, together with cadmium sulphide (CdS) and cuprous oxide (Cu_2O). For thermoelectric applications, the compounds lead sulphide (PbS), lead selenide (PbSe) and lead telluride (PbTe) are of particular interest. The most important properties of the semiconductors most commonly met with today are therefore given in Table 4, pp. 74–75. in which the symbols used have the following meanings.

μ_n, μ_p the mobilities of negative (n) and positive (p) charge carriers (electrons and defect electrons) in $cm^2/V\ s$

ΔE the bandwidth of the forbidden zone between the valence and conduction bands in electron volts (eV)

$\dfrac{d\Delta E}{dT}$ the temperature coefficient of the bandwidth in eV/deg.

ΔE_{st} the distance between the impurity level and the upper edge of the valence band or the lower edge of the conduction band (within the forbidden zone) in eV

ρ the specific resistance in ohm cm (Ωcm)

$\left(\dfrac{\Delta\rho}{\rho}\right)_H$ the relative change in resistance in a magnetic field H in %

R_H the Hall coefficient in cm³/A s

L_n the mean free path for the diffusion of electrons in cm

τ_n the life of an electron in s

D_n the diffusion coefficient of electrons at $T = 300°$ K in cm²/s

$\left(\dfrac{m_{\text{eff}}}{m_e}\right)_{n,p}$ the relative mass of electrons (n) and defect electrons (p) in %

λ_0 the wave-length of the optical absorption threshold in mμ

n_{opt} the optical refractive index

α the thermoelectric e.m.f. in μV/deg.

a the lattice constant in Ångström units (Å 10^{-8} cm)

T_S the melting point in °C

All the values given in Table 4 relate to pure substances. Some come from original works and more extensive tables, but some of them were calculated with the aid of equations 3.3a, 3.3.h and $\lambda_0 = hc/e\Delta E$ (cf. equation 3.8b). These values are indicated by an asterisk.

The types of crystal lattice in which the most important semiconductors in the table crystallize are given in *Figure 17a–h*. *Figure 17a* (diamond type) shows the same lattice as *Figure 6* in a different way; the elementary cubic cells correspond to each other.

When we compare the standard semiconductors germanium and silicon, with which we are already familiar, the first thing to strike us is that germanium has a narrower bandwidth and higher mobilities than silicon. From these facts we can draw some interesting conclusions regarding the photoelectric applications of these elements. The narrower bandwidth corresponds to a lower value of the energy of light required to raise photoelectrically liberated electrons across the forbidden zone into the conduction band. But it also means that the absorption constant, and with it the threshold wave-length for the photoelectric effect, corresponds to longer wave-lengths for germanium than for silicon. Germanium photocells are

71

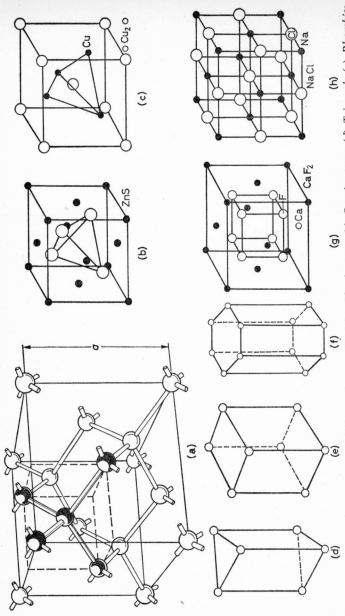

Figure 17. Crystal structures: (a) Diamond type; (b) Zinc blende type; (c) Cuprite type; (d) Trigonal; (e) Rhombic; (f) Hexagonal; (g) Fluorspar type; (h) Rock-salt type

therefore much more sensitive to red than are silicon ones. But silicon photocells have the advantage that their sensitivity range agrees better with the energy distribution in the spectrum of sunlight. That portion of the sun's radiation which has maximum energy has a wave-length of 627 mμ. Consequently photoelements of pure silicon single crystals containing a p–n-junction are able to convert the energy of the sun's radiation into electrical energy with an efficiency of 10 per cent and more, and they have been used very successfully, for example, to supply artificial satellites with electrical energy.

The crystal lattices of the $A^{III}B^{V}$ compounds are very similar to those of germanium and silicon. Not only are these compounds similar in many ways to germanium and silicon, but they have properties which make them suitable for special applications, particularly indium antimonide (InSb) and indium arsenide (InAs), which are distinguished by high electron mobilities and high rates of change of resistance in magnetic fields; this latter property is much greater than for bismuth. These two substances are therefore preferred in the construction of electromagnetic amplifiers (*see* p. 120).

The high rate of change of resistance of InSb and InAs in a magnetic field is explained by their high mobilities, which in their turn can only be understood by consideration of the nature of the forbidden zone from the crystal-structure aspect. Hitherto, we have used a highly simplified diagram of the band model, in which we assumed that the width of the forbidden zone is constant. In reality, its width is to differing extents affected by the lattice structure. According to Herman's theory of band structure, in which both the conduction band and the valence bands are constructed of sub-bands, and the heteropolar nature of the $A^{III}B^{V}$ compounds is allowed for by a distortion calculation, the forbidden zones in Si, Ge, GaAs, and InSb have the shape shown in *Figure 18*. The energy E is there shown as a function of the wave number k_e. The effective mass can be deduced in a simple way from this relationship by means of equation 4.3e. The mobility depends on the mass (equation 3.3e). The interrelation between the two equations

Table 4. Constants

| | | | | | | | Physical | | |
Sub-stance	μ_n (cm²/V s)	μ_p (cm²/V s)	ΔE (eV)	$\dfrac{d\Delta E}{dT}$ (eV/°)	ΔE_{St} (eV)	ρ (Ωcm)	$\left(\dfrac{\Delta\rho}{\rho}\right)^{\%}_H$ $H=$ $10^4\,G\beta$	R_H (cm³/A s)	L_n (cm)
C	1,800	1,200	5·3	—	—	5.10^{14}	—	—	4.10^{-5}
Ge	3,900	1,700	0·72	$-3·5.10^{-4}$	0·015	50	30	-10^5	$4·5.10^{-}$
Si	1,900	425	1·12	$-3·6.10^{-4}$	0·08	$2·3.10^5$	—	-10^8	8.10^{-3}
Se	—	1	2·2	$-4·5.10^{-4}$	—	10^6	—	$+10^6$	7.10^{-4*} (
Te	1,750	1,250	0·32	$-1·64.10^{-4}$	—	$1·1.10^4$	—	-10^3	—
Bi	5,000	—	—	—	—	10^{-4}	45	-6	—
InSb	77,000	1,250	0·26	$-2·9.10^{-4}$	0·007	$1·6.10^{-3}$	2,360	-10^3	5.10^{-3}
GaSb	4,000	2,000	0·80	$-4·1.10^{-4}$	0·03	10^{-2}	—	-50	—
AlSb	200	200	1·6	$-3·5.10^{-4}$	—	—	—	—	2.10^{-3}
InAs	27,000	280	0·34	$-3·5.10^{-4}$	0·01	2.10^{-1}	450	-10^4	1.10^{-2}
GaAs	4,000	240	1·38	$-4·9.10^{-4}$	0·31	2.10^{-2}	—	-5.10^2	8.10^{-3}
InP	3,400	650	1·25	$-4·6.10^{-4}$	—	10^{-1}	—	-3.10^4	$1·3.10^{-2}$
CdS	240	—	2·5	$-4·7.10^{-4}$	0·02	10^9	—	-10^3	3.10^{-3}
Sb₂S₃	—	—	2·0	—	0·98	$\sim10^4$	—	—	—
PbS	640	350	0·37	$-2·5.10^{-4}$	—	50	—	-10^2	2.10^{-3}
PbSe	1,400	640	0·45	$-2·5.10^{-4}$	—	14*	117	-10^2	5.10^{-3*}
PbTe	2,100	840	0·54	$-2·5.10^{-4}$	—	2·1*	—	-10^3	4.10^{-3*}
Cu₂O	250	57	2·06	—	0·6	5.10^6	—	$+8.10^6$	—
UO₂	15	10	—	—	—	20	—	$+1$	—

SEMICONDUCTING SUBSTANCES

emiconductor Materials

Properties

τ_n (s)	D_n (cm² s⁻¹)	$\left(\dfrac{m_{eff}}{m_e}\right)$%		λ_0 (mµ)	n_{opt}	α (μV/°)	a (Å)	T_S (°C)	Crystal type
		n	p						
8.10⁻⁹	45*	—	—	220	2·47	—	3·56	3,540 (subl.)	diamond
6.10⁻³	93	25	—	1,600	3·95	500	5·65	958	diamond
2·1.10⁻⁶	31	80	—	980	3·44	400	5·42	1,414	diamond
2.10⁻⁵(p)	2·5.10⁻²(p)	—	—	540*	2·56	1,000	4·34	220	hexagonal
—	44*	68	91	3,800*	4·8	180	4·45	452	spiral
—	125*	—	—	—	—	60	4·74	271	trigonal
2·7.10⁻⁷	93	3·7	18	8,000	4·02	340	6·45	523	zinc blende
—	100*	27	—	1,800	3·71	1,500	6·09	702	zinc blende
2.10⁻⁴	40*	—	—	750	3·0	—	6·10	1,065	zinc blende
7.10⁻⁶	14*	6·4	33	3,500	3·25	400	6·06	936	zinc blende
9.10⁻⁹	70*	—	—	910	3·20	—	5·63	1,280	zinc blende
2.10⁻⁶	80*	—	—	950	3·00	—	—	1,070	zinc blende
1·5.10⁻⁶*	6*	20	—	480*	3·41	750	5·82	1,750	zinc blende
—	—	—	—	800*	3·19	—	—	546	rhombic
2·5.10⁻⁷*	16*	—	—	3,000	3·91	400	5·91	1,114	cubic
6.10⁻⁷	35*	—	—	3,000*	—	200	6·14	1,065	cubic
8.10⁻⁷	52*	—	—	4,000	—	110	6·44	917	cubic
—	6*	—	—	800	2·71	1,500	4·26	1,110	cuprite
—	4*	—	—	—	—	—	5·47	2,227	fluorspar

SEMICONDUCTORS

gives the following relationship between the mobility and the curvature (d^2E/dk_i^2) of the edges of the bands at the forbidden zone:

$$\mu_n = \frac{1}{2}\frac{e\tau}{h^2}\frac{d^2E}{dk_e^2} \qquad \ldots (6.1)$$

This equation states that the greater the curvature of the edge of the band, the greater will be the mobility of the electrons. This explains not only the unusually high mobilities of InSb, in *Figure 18*, but also the fact that the

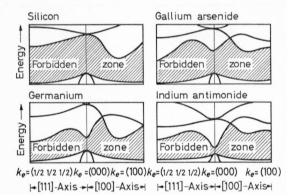

$k_e = (1/2\ 1/2\ 1/2)\ k_e = (000)\ k_e = (100)\ k_e = (1/2\ 1/2\ 1/2)\ k_e = (000)\quad k_e = (100)$
⊢[111]-Axis⊣⊢[100]-Axis⊣   ⊢[111]-Axis⊣⊢[100]-Axis⊣

Figure 18. Energy bands of Si, Ge, GaAs *and* InSb
as related to their crystal structure

mobilities of Si are lower than those of Ge. The curvature of the edges of the bands is subject to severe fluctuations as also is the width of the forbidden zones. The Boltzmann distribution of energy should result in easier thermal excitation if the forbidden zone is narrow, thus making more electrons available in the conduction band (3.5f). Both these effects are in fact found in InSb: sharp curvature of the bands, and a narrow forbidden zone; which result in the presence of a large number of electrons with high mobilities.

SEMICONDUCTING SUBSTANCES

The three lead compounds mentioned in Table 4 (PbS, PbSe and PbTe) also have electrons and holes with relatively high mobilities. But their low thermal conductivities are more important for their thermoelectric properties. For, according to equation 3.6b, the factor $\alpha^2\sigma/\kappa$, which is also called the thermoelectric effectiveness, or figure of merit, is a measure of the suitability of the substance for thermoelectric applications. Physically, the figure of merit represents the ratio of the electric power to the thermal power per degree and per unit volume.

The lead compounds mentioned form alloys with each other, and also with bismuth and antimony tellurides (Bi_2Te_3, Sb_2Te_3), and all these alloys are suitable for thermoelectric applications, as they have relatively low thermal conductivities, between 5 and $9\cdot10^{-3}$ cal/cm s deg. Just now, compounds having the structure $A^{II}B^{IV}C_2^V$ are being regarded with great interest from the point of view of thermoelectric applications, because their thermoelectric e.m.f.'s have a lower temperature coefficient, and are of the order of 300 μV/deg. even at temperatures of around 100° K.

The relation between the bandwidth and the optical absorption threshold can also be particularly well studied in solid solutions. For example, solid solutions of GaAs and GaP of the form $GaAs_yP_{1-y}$, have properties as shown in Table 5.

Table 5. Bandwidth and Optical Properties of $Ga(As_yP_{1-y})$ Solid Solutions

	y			
	0	0·2	0·4	0·6
ΔE (eV)	2·24	2·20	2·10	1·82
λ_0 (mμ)	560	570	590	680
Transparent colour	reddish	yellowish	greenish	bluish

If the width of the forbidden zone is considerable, this means that the lattice bond is strong and the mobility of the charge carriers low, in accordance with our corpuscular model (*see* p. 34 ff.) and, correspondingly, if the forbidden zone is narrow (low bandwidth ΔE), the lattice bond will be weak and the mobilities high. In homopolar lattices (covalent bonds, e.g. diamond, germanium, silicon) the energies of the bonds are particularly high, whereas heteropolar lattices have as a rule lower bonding energies (ionic bonds, e.g. $A^{III}B^V$ compounds; *see also* Table 4). At present, as a working rule, we are inclined to attribute the observed differences to a predominance of the covalent type of bond when high bandwidths are observed, and the determination of a narrow bandwidth is considered as evidence that the ionic bond is preferred.

Antimony trisulphide (Sb_2S_3) in Table 4, together with cadmium sulphide (CdS), has been used to make signal plates in television camera tubes. Deposited in a thin layer from the vapour state, it has good longitudinal conductance but low transverse conductance, so that illuminated portions of the layer can remain charged for the duration of the contact process, but the signal is quickly passed on by the conducting supporting layer. The specific resistance of the very thin layers (only a few μ; $\mu = 10^{-4}$ cm) is about 10^{12} Ωcm.

Radiation begins to be absorbed at a threshold wave-length λ_0, because the energy of the quanta of radiation is then sufficient to liberate electrons from the atomic bonds (the photoelectric effect). Semiconductors are therefore transparent to light of longer wave-lengths, and can be used as filters in the infra-red region of the spectrum on account of the steepness of the absorption threshold. They are much superior to the alkali halide filters previously used, which are soluble in water and hygroscopic, for they are stable in the presence of water, organic solvents and even weak acids. Their hardness and brittleness enable them to take a good polish and to be given good optical surfaces.

7

METHODS OF PREPARATION AND PRODUCTION

THE processes for obtaining single crystals of semiconducting substances in as pure a state as possible all follow the same general pattern: first, the chemical production of the substance; second, remelting and purification; and finally, the growth of single crystals.

The chemical methods of production will of course differ for each substance; they will be discussed later, for several important semiconductors (*see* p. 85 ff.).

The method of purification generally used is zone melting. This depends on the fact that when a liquid freezes, any impurity atoms it contains will become a solid aggregate either sooner or later than the pure matrix. If sooner, the impurity atoms will come out of solution and their concentration in the matrix will be lowered; if later, the pure substance will become enriched in impurity atoms. The ratio of the proportion of impurities in the solidified crystal to their proportion in the liquid is called the segregation constant of the impurity in question. If the impurities come out of solution, the segregation constant is less than unity; if the solution becomes enriched, it is greater than unity. For example, the segregation constant of antimony (Sb) in germanium (Ge) is 0·0025; i.e. that part of the liquid which solidifies last becomes enriched in Sb. When a substance is to be zone melted, it is subjected to fractional crystallization, in the form of bars, in a special furnace, in which—generally by high-frequency heating—a narrow zone only is allowed to melt, and this zone moves through the bar. *Plate 1* shows that the furnace may be moved up and down the bar. The portion of the substance in the hot zone becomes liquid, and then solidifies again as soon as it has left the hot zone. If it is assumed that the substance in *Plate 1* moves from left to right, and that the segregation constant of some of the impurities is less than 1, these will be carried from the molten zone up to the front of the bar, while the back becomes enriched in impurities whose segregation constant is greater than 1. Both ends can now be sawn off, and the central portion zone-melted once again. This can be repeated several times, resulting in such high purities (with Ge, for instance) that the concentration of the residual impurities can no longer be detected either chemically or spectroscopically, but only by conductivity measurements. With Ge, a figure of 1 atom of impurity to 10^{10} atoms of Ge can be reached. The purified metal is generally polycrystalline in structure (*but see* p. 88).

A good method which has been discovered for growing single crystals is to dip in a seed crystal and then pull the single crystal out from the molten material. *Figure 19* shows

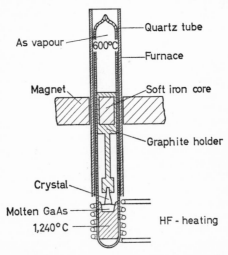

Figure 19. Apparatus for drawing single crystals of $A^{III}B^{V}$ compounds with high vapour pressures in the liquid state

an apparatus for pulling single crystals, which is also suitable for melts having a high vapour pressure, such as many of the $A^{III}B^{V}$ compounds, for example. In this apparatus, pure polycrystalline GaAs is melted in a closed quartz tube in a graphite crucible heated by high-frequency induction. With the aid of a magnetic mechanism, a single crystal is placed in the melt as a 'seed' and a single crystal of GaAs is slowly withdrawn, at constant speed and rotating all the time. In the case illustrated, to maintain the vapour pressure of the arsenic at a value corresponding to the melting point, the vessel (the quartz tube) needs an extra heating furnace. The reason for the preparation of single crystals is that only in single crystals can junctions be made which will have predictable properties. In polycrystals, uncontrolled junction effects may occur at the interior grain boundaries, even in the purest semiconductors. Substances having a low vapour pressure in the molten state, such as Ge, are worked under a protective atmosphere or in a vacuum (*Plate 2*).

In working with many molten semiconducting substances it must be remembered that the volume of the crystal grown is 7–14 per cent greater than that of the melt, and danger to the vessel when the melt solidifies must be avoided. The increase in volume on crystallization results from the fact that the crystal lattice represents the loosest possible stable spherical packing, whereas the melt represents the closest possible spherical packing.

For the production of junctions having particular properties, known concentrations of impurity atoms are introduced into the semiconducting material. Semiconductor diodes, triodes (transistors) and tetrodes are made in this way. Three methods are used, viz.: (1) A melting method, in which impurity atoms are added to the liquid; (2) An alloying method, in which the matrix material is alloyed with impurity elements; (3) A diffusion method, in which the impurity atoms are allowed to diffuse into the lattice of the matrix material.

The advantage of the first method is that it can be combined directly with the growth of the single crystals. Definite quantities of impurity atoms (donors and acceptors) can be added to the melt—it is doped with them, as we say—and in this

SEMICONDUCTORS

way the single crystal drawn out of the melt will have pre-determined conduction properties. By alternate doping, layers having different types of conduction (*n*-, *p*-conduction) can be formed in the same crystal. The charge carriers thermally generated in one layer are retained as minority carriers in the next layer, to which other majority carriers are added by adding further impurity atoms from the source. The concentration of acceptors in the second layer must therefore exceed that of the donors in the first layer, if the first is *n*-conducting and the second is *p*-conducting (*Figure 20b*).

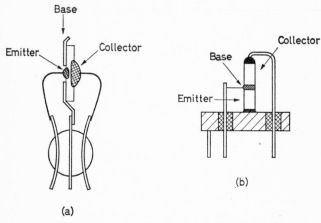

Figure 20. Structures of transistors: (a) Alloyed; (b) Grown

The second method, alloying, utilizes the fact that, according to equation 3.3g, lattice 'bricks', i.e. atoms or ions of the matrix lattice, can diffuse into each other when different substances are adjacent to each other. Table 6 gives the diffusion coefficients D_0 for a series of elements in germanium —particularly elements of the third and fifth columns of the periodic table, which are used as donors or acceptors.

The relation 3.3i enables the diffusion coefficient to be calculated for the actual temperature at which the alloying process takes place. For example, if a germanium crystal is

PREPARATION AND PRODUCTION

alloyed with indium, a drop of indium is applied to both sides of an n-conducting wafer of monocrystalline germanium, and they are heated together to about 500° C. Then indium atoms diffuse from both sides—from the state of solid aggre-

Table 6. Diffusion Coefficients D_0 for Various Elements in Ge and Si

D_0 (cm^{2}s^{-1})	Element								
	Ge	Ga	In	P	As	Sb	Bi	Au	He
in Ge	7·8	34	0·15	3·3	2·1	1·2	4·7	18	0·0065
in Si	—	3·3	16	1,400	0·44	4·0	2,200	0·0095	0·11

gation—into the germanium, and produce a p-conducting layer on both sides. The p-conducting layer is allowed to proceed until only a narrow region of n-conduction remains in the centre as a base zone (*Figure 20a*). As already explained (*see* p. 66 ff.), the thickness of the base layer determines the limiting frequency of the transistor. The thinner this layer, the higher will be the limiting frequency. A very favourable form has the mesa transistor. One method of alloying, which enables base layers to be made having thicknesses down to 2μ,

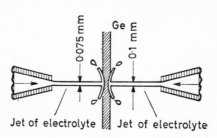

Figure 21. Electrolytic method of etching to make diffusion transistors

is electrolytic etching (*Figure 21*). In the same operation, indium is electrodeposited on both sides of the leaf of Ge, diffuses into the thin basis layer and forms p-conducting barrier layers (surface barrier transistor). The limiting frequency of such a transistor is of order 50 Mc/s.

The third method also utilizes the phenomenon of diffusion. Unlike the alloying method, however, the impurity atoms which diffuse into the solid matrix are this time in the gaseous phase. This method is therefore called the diffusion method. The matrix substance—preferably Ge or Si—is brought into an atmosphere of gaseous acceptors or donors or both, at a high temperature, with the result that the diffusion of impurity atoms into the matrix substance is much more uniform than in the alloying process, in which diffusion is from the solid phase. *Plates 3* and *4* show sections of Si, photographed with oblique illumination, in which the layers having different conductivities in which, e.g., n-conduction has become p-conduction (inversion layer), are revealed by etching with hydrofluoric acid to which traces of dilute nitric acid have been added. These pictures show how homogeneous such layers are. In the examples shown in *Plates 3* and *4*, the thicknesses of the base zones of the transistor have been measured optically and found to be $3\cdot5\mu$ and $4\cdot5\mu$. The different rates of diffusion (*see* Table 4) enable acceptors and donors to diffuse into the matrix substance simultaneously, which accelerates the manufacturing process. In the alloying method, part of the original substance, with constant density of impurity atoms, remains as the base layer; but when the diffusion process is used the base layer has a variable impurity density, which, from the diffusion equation (3.3g), decreases exponentially with the depth of penetration into the matrix. The diffusion method is therefore especially suitable for making drift transistors (*see* p. 68), which have a particularly high cut-off frequency of order 500 Mc/s, because the field in the base zone, which results from the variable density of impurity centres, accelerates the passage of charge carriers across this zone.

The methods of preparing the more important substances are now discussed separately.

Germanium (Ge). The method of preparing germanium is shown diagrammatically in *Figure 22*. The raw material is the ore germanite, which contains 6–8 per cent Ge. It is ground

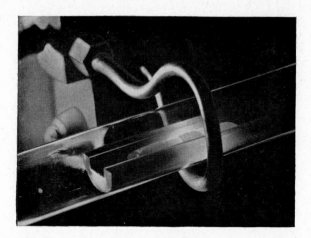

Plate 1. Zone melting process (horizontal, with Ge in a graphite crucible)

(After Salow and Hähnlein)

Plate 2. Drawing a single crystal of Ge out of the melt

(After Goorissen, J., *Philips Techn. Rundschau*, 1959–60, **21,** No. 7)

[*To face p. 84*

Plate 3. Section through the transition regions of junctions (inversion layers): p–n–p-transistor

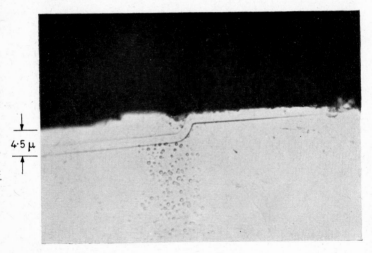

Plate 4. Section through the transition regions of junctions (inversion layers): n–p–n-transistor

PREPARATION AND PRODUCTION

down and treated with hydrochloric acid which brings the GeO_2 in the ore into the form of a distillable compound, germanium tetrachloride ($GeCl_4$). Distillation, of which a single stage only is drawn in the diagram, is actually repeated several times, and the fractional distillation enables the $GeCl_4$ to be more or less purified. The further addition of chlorine

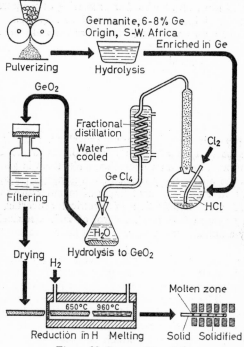

Figure 22. Preparation of Ge
(After Hühn, C. F., *Telefunken-Z.*, 1958, **31**, No. 119)

gas is for the special purpose of removing arsenic, which otherwise remains in the form of arsenic trichloride, but which is converted by the addition of chlorine into a compound difficult to vaporize. The $GeCl_4$, thus purified, is then turned

G

85

back into GeO_2 by hydrolysis according to the reaction

$$GeCl_4 + 2H_2O \longrightarrow GeO_2 + 4HCl \qquad \ldots (7.1)$$

The GeO_2 is filtered, dried and finally reduced to germanium with super-pure hydrogen at 650° C; the precipitated powder is melted into bars at 960° C, and these bars are then subjected to zone melting (see p. 79).

Figure 23 illustrates the further processing of the pure zone-melted material into semiconductor diodes. The bars of Ge are first sawn up and melted. Single crystals are drawn out of the melt by the method described on page 80; they are cut into discs 0·2 mm thick which are divided into smaller pieces of area $1·2 \times 1·2$ mm². The relative sizes of the single crystal and the square pieces used in Ge diodes can be seen from Plate 5. The junction, which in this case consists of a transition (inversion) layer from the n-conducting Ge which surrounds the tungsten tip placed on it to the p-conducting Ge (see p. 65), is made in a forming machine. This equipment tests the characteristic curves of the diodes made by heat treatment, and, in another operation, melts them in glass tubes in which the diodes are protected from atmospheric corrosion by a protective gas. The next stages of manufacture shown in Figure 23 are: stabilization of electrical properties of the diodes by aging (tempering), control of their electrical coefficients by automatic measurements, and their encapsulation.

Silicon (Si). Chemically pure silicon is very much more difficult to prepare than pure germanium. Silicon—at least in the molten state—is extremely aggressive chemically, and attacks crucibles of any material, so that impurity atoms from the crucible are always found in the melt. Although there exists a very promising reaction for the preparation of pure silicon—starting with SiO_2, which is mixed with magnesium and reduced at red heat in a graphite crucible—a reaction which starts from a gaseous silicon compound is preferred in practice. Silicon tetrachloride, $SiCl_4$, is used; in the Dupont process it is reduced by means of zinc vapour according to the following equation

$$SiCl_4 + 2Zn \longrightarrow Si + 2ZnCl_2 \qquad \ldots (7.2a)$$

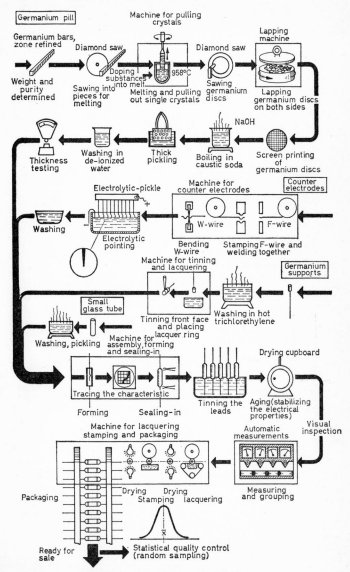

Figure 23. Preparation of Ge *diodes*
(After Hühn, C. F., *Telefunken-Z.*, 1958, **31**, No. 119)

SEMICONDUCTORS

To reduce the $SiCl_4$, aluminium and hydrogen can also be used according to the reaction equations:

$$3SiCl_4 + 4Al \longrightarrow 3Si + 4AlCl_3 \qquad \dots (7.2b)$$

and

$$SiCl_4 + 2H_2 \longrightarrow Si + 4HCl \qquad \dots (7.2c)$$

In addition, pure silicon can be prepared by the thermal decomposition of SiH_4 and the dissociation of SiI_4 in a vacuum. The equations for these are:

$$SiH_4 \longrightarrow Si + 2H_2 \qquad \dots (7.2d)$$

and

$$SiI_4 \longrightarrow Si + 2I_2 \qquad \dots (7.2e)$$

The thermal reactions—particularly the Dupont process—take place at red-hot surfaces, e.g. at the walls of a quartz furnace, or at surfaces of graphite, tungsten, tantalum or even glowing silicon itself. Pure silicon is precipitated as a powder.

Methods in which silicon is extracted from one of its compounds in gaseous form have the advantage that no molten silicon comes into contact with any crucible material at melting temperatures, which prevents the silicon from being con-

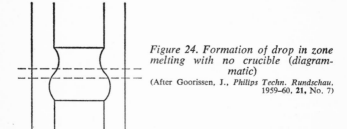

Figure 24. Formation of drop in zone melting with no crucible (diagrammatic)

(After Goorissen, J., *Philips Techn. Rundschau*, 1959–60, **21**, No. 7)

taminated by impurity atoms, with consequent uncontrollable conduction behaviour. The brown silicon powder obtained in this way is sintered into rods. These rods are then subjected to zone melting. The zone-melting process described above for germanium (p. 79) is not suitable for silicon on account of its chemical reactivity, and a process which does not use a crucible has had to be developed. In this, the melt and the furnace move past each other, not horizontally but vertically. The molten zone, in the form of a drop, is held, by the strong surface tension, between the two ends of the rod (*Figure 24*). The rod is rotated during zone melting. The high-frequency furnace (a loop of wire in *Plate 6*) is moved up and down along the rotating rod, which is in a glass cylinder filled with a protective gas atmosphere. The drop of molten material thus moves through the rod. The polycrystalline sintered silicon usually becomes monocrystalline after repeated zone melting. Even without any seed crystal, the preferred direction of growth is the (111) axis, which can be seen externally, as the rod assumes a hexagonal section. To prevent any contact between molten silicon and crucible materials when seeding with impurity atoms, either the alloying method or the diffusion method is preferable in making semiconducting components with several boundary layers (e.g. transistors) (*see* p. 81 ff.).

Indium antimonide (InSb). Of the $A^{III}B^V$ compounds, InSb has proved itself to be just as good as Ge and Si. The best way of preparing it chemically is by melting together stoichiometric quantities of In and Sb. The resultant substance is remelted, purified by zone melting, and single crystals are drawn from the melt, all under an atmosphere of argon. Graphite, or quartz covered with a layer of carbon, is used for crucibles. In zone melting, the front end of the bar generally shows p-type conduction and the back end n-type. This means that the acceptor impurities in InSb have a segregation constant less than 1 and the donors have a segregation constant greater than 1. The single crystals drawn from the melt have generally grown in the (111) direction. The rate of growth is said to be 2 cm/h, the rate of rotation of the crystal during drawing 100 rev/min. Zone melting is continued until a figure of 1 impurity atom per 10^{13} atoms of InSb is reached. Owing to the high mobilities of the charge carriers in InSb (cf. Table 4, pp. 74–75), it shows unusually strong electromagnetic effects (see Table 1, p. 20). In order to make practical use of these effects, it is a good idea to prepare very thin layers of InSb so that when they are placed in a magnetic field the magnetic resistance will be as low as possible. There is a limit to which the thickness of a compact material can be reduced mechanically, so that thin layers are now prepared by evaporation. It has been found necessary to evaporate indium and antimony from separate evaporators on to a support preheated to 400° C, and to select the vaporization temperatures in such a way that the constituents of the compound are in stoichiometric ratio on the support. The layers prepared in this way have properties almost as good as those of the compact substance.

Gallium antimonide (GaSb). The behaviour of GaSb resembles that of InSb. So far, however, it has proved impossible to prepare in sufficiently pure form, so that at present there is little prospect of its practical application.

Aluminium antimonide (AlSb). Aluminium antimonide has a very wide forbidden zone, $\Delta E = 1.6$ eV, so that it appears to be extremely suitable for making photocells. AlSb is also prepared by the simultaneous melting of stoichiometric quantities of its constituents, but this is rendered more difficult by the tendency of the Al to react with the material of the crucible. Thus small quantities of Al_4C_3 are formed in a graphite crucible, and it would be desirable to use crucibles of sintered Al_2O_3, but the melt easily sticks hard to its rough inner face. A practical disadvantage of AlSb is that it corrodes extremely easily. In damp air, it decomposes into a black powder within a few days, the Al being converted into hydroxide by H_2O. Unfortunately, the degree of purity attainable so far—1 impurity atom to 10^{16} atoms of pure AlSb—is not good enough to be able to say that the conduction properties have been mastered.

Indium arsenide (InAs), *gallium arsenide* (GaAs), *indium phosphide* (InP). The antimonides discussed above possess only a low vapour pressure at their melting point, so that in the molten state they very much resemble Ge and Si, but the arsenides and phosphides of the $A^{III}B^{V}$ compounds have a

PREPARATION AND PRODUCTION

high vapour pressure over the melt. This equilibrium vapour pressure of a compound melting in a closed crucible must be maintained during solidification. This is done by introducing an excess of the more volatile component of the compound (As, P) into the vapour chamber, by the accurate weighing out of the right excess amount, in making the compound from stoichiometric quantities of its components. In this case, a sufficient excess of the more volatile component must be weighed out to preserve the vapour pressure. Similar precautions must be taken in the remelting, zone melting and drawing of the single crystal (*see* p. 80, *Figure 19*). InAs, like InSb, is also particularly useful on account of its strong electromagnetic effects. GaAs, because of the favourable position of its optical absorption threshold (*see* Table 4, pp. 74–75), has great possibilities of utilization for the photocells in solar batteries and nowadays also as a special kind of maser (*see* p. 124), an injection-maser. The preparation of InP at present involves difficult technical problems. The equilibrium vapour pressure of P above its melt amounts to 60 kg/cm^2. All the methods of treating molten InP therefore involve great danger of explosion if such a high pressure has to be maintained in a closed crucible. This danger can however be lessened by working with a non-stoichiometric ratio, giving a lower vapour pressure (15–20 kg/cm^2) for the more volatile component.

8

SOME PARTICULAR COMPONENTS
MADE OF SEMICONDUCTORS

RIGHT at the beginning we learnt that one of the most important properties of semiconductors is the fact that their electrical conductivity increases with temperature. This has been known for longer than any of their other properties, and for a long time was considered to be a criterion of a semiconductor. The simplest way, too, of using semiconductors is as temperature-dependent resistors [thermistors, or NTC resistors (NTC = Negative Temperature Coefficient)]. These are used to trap surges of current on switching on, as temperature-sensitive switch elements for measuring temperature or quantity of heat—especially in combination with bridge circuits—and to measure changes of state, on cooling, in liquids in which they are immersed.

But the resistance of a semiconductor generally depends not only on the temperature but also on its illumination. As has already been seen (pp. 1, 2), the photoconductivity of selenium was discovered a long time ago, and directed attention to the whole group of substances. Nowadays, cadmium sulphide (CdS) is the material most often used for photoresistors. Layers of pure Cd, 30–50 μ thick, which have been deposited from the vapour in a high vacuum and contain cupric chloride ($CuCl_2$) as impurity centres, with an effective surface area of 30 mm², placed between comb-shaped electrodes, show a change of resistance under an illumination of 1,500 lux of about a million times, from 10^9 Ω in the dark to 10^3 Ω in the light.

The use of semiconductor diodes as rectifiers has already been mentioned (p. 53 ff.). Their ability to alter their capacitance in the reverse direction with applied reverse voltage (p. 56 ff.), and their consequent suitability for use in parametric amplifiers (p. 127), have earned them the name of varactors—varistors for this particular application.

Diodes which make particular use of the sensitivity of semiconductors to light are called photodiodes (*see* p. 60 ff.). The photo-e.m.f. resulting from the photoelectric effect makes the photodiode a photocell. The wider the forbidden zone, the greater will be the photo-e.m.f. Silicon (p. 73) is therefore preferred as a semiconductor for photocells, but gallium arsenide (p. 91) is also used.

Of the semiconductor triodes, the point transistor (p. 64), the junction transistor (p. 63), the surface-barrier transistor (p. 83), the tunnel transistor (p. 68), the mesa transistor (p. 83) and the drift transistor (p. 68) have all been mentioned, and Shockley's filamentary transistor and unipolar transistor are now dealt with.

The filamentary transistor (*Figure 25*) consists of a

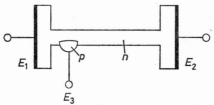

Figure 25. Filamentary transistor

germanium crystal in the form of a filament, which is n-conducting and has electrodes (E_1, E_2) which have large surface areas. At E_3 a p-conducting zone has been made by the alloying method. The filamentary transistor is now of historical interest, for it merely served to demonstrate whether, with a weak negative bias on electrode E_3, for which the p-conducting layer is still positive with respect to its n-conducting surroundings, holes can penetrate the base material and reduce its resistance (injection of minority carriers).

In the unipolar transistor (*Figure 26*), the space charge produced by the field at the junctions (barrier layers) affects the current flowing through the n-conducting Ge, and controls it in the same way as the grid of a thermionic valve controls the flow of electrons from the cathode. Since the junction is connected with reverse bias there is no injection of minority carriers. The resistance in the control circuit is very

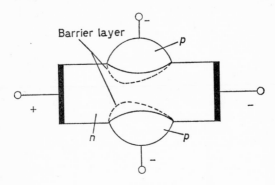

Figure 26. Unipolar transistor

high, and ohmic, of the order of several megohms, and is thus comparable with the high grid resistance of a valve. The whole behaviour of a unipolar transistor resembles that of a pentode valve, but the mutual conductance is low.

The possibility has already been mentioned of making semiconductor tetrodes (p. 68). The four-layer transistor (*Figure 27*) is generally used as a diode switch or triode

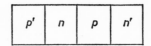

Figure 27. Arrangement of the layers in a four-layer transistor

switch. As a diode switch it may be supposed to work as follows (*Figure 28*). With the polarity shown in the diagram, a barrier layer forms at the central n–p-junction. As the barrier voltage increases, the Zener effect finally occurs, leading to a breakdown of the high resistance of the barrier

COMPONENTS MADE OF SEMICONDUCTORS

(*see* p. 54). Thereafter the layers p' and n' at each side act as suppliers of carriers, so that the voltage on the transistor drops to a residual voltage which is merely the potential difference across the resistance of the transistor, which in this mode of

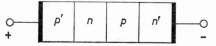

Figure 28. Diode switch

operation is low. The characteristic of a diode switch resembles that of a glow discharge. The triode switch differs from the diode switch in the same way as a glow discharge tube differs from a thyratron. The third electrode (base) enables the switching process to be controlled (*Figure 29*).

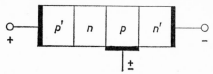

Figure 29. Triode switch

Salow's transistor switch can also be equated with a semiconductor tetrode, although it is a three-zone transistor in which a tungsten point electrode is incorporated as fourth electrode (*Figure 30a*). This tungsten tip penetrates the spherical collector of an n–p–n-alloy transistor and touches

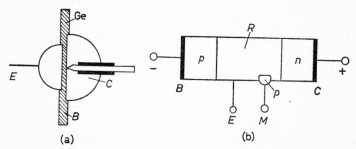

(a)   (b)

Figure 30. Semiconductor triodes with three layers: (a) Transistor switch; (b) Spacistor

95

the surface of the Ge crystal. The extra emission of electrons from the tip when the potential of the collector is positive means that the transistor is quickly brought into a highly conducting state when the potential of the emitter has been dropping for only a short time. When the emitter is blocked, which need only be done for a short time, the field in front of the tungsten tip rises again, so that the transistor returns to its original (barrier) state. The switching time is of the order of 10^{-1} µsec. The reverse resistance is 100,000 times as great as the forward resistance.

Another semiconductor tetrode with three layers is the spacistor (*Figure 30b*). The third, middle layer consists of a zone R of space charge between the p and n zones of a $p-n$-transition. In this part of the crystal the field strength is high. Additional electrons are injected into it by means of a point contact (emitter E) and are removed by the collector. This current can be controlled by means of a fourth, p-conducting, electrode (the modulator M). Since this latter acts as a screening grid, the internal resistance can assume values of up to 30 MΩ. With the spacistor, therefore, a voltage can be amplified up to 10^3 times. Owing to the drift effect of the space charge zone, it has a critical limiting frequency of 100 Mc/s.

Finally mention is made of the phototransistor. This may be considered as a photodiode with an amplifier connected behind it. It can have a sensitivity of up to 30 times that of a photodiode. *Figure 31* illustrates the mode of operation of a

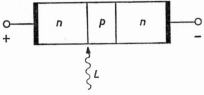

Figure 31. Phototransistor

phototransistor. The transistor is run with an open base. In the example shown, the light (L) falling on it influences the barrier layer at the collector.

9

CHARACTERISTICS AND CIRCUITS

IN EXPLAINING how transistors work (p. 65), we have already
discussed, in some detail, analogies with the mode of operation of thermionic valves, and compared the grounded-emitter,
grounded-base and grounded-collector circuits with the
grounded-cathode, grounded-grid and grounded-anode circuits
of a valve (*Figure 16*, p. 67). But we have already seen that
one essential difference between transistors and valves is that
the transistor cannot be controlled without loss of power.
Whereas in a valve the current in the control circuit is so
small that it can be considered as zero to a first approximation,
the corresponding current in a transistor cannot be neglected.
In each circuit element with an input circuit and an output
circuit, two coefficients per circuit suffice to describe the
electrical behaviour of the element (cf. p. 109). With valves,
since the current in the input circuit (control circuit) is
negligible, only two coefficients are needed to describe the
behaviour of the valve (e.g. its internal resistance and the
slope of the characteristic). But since the current in the input
circuit of a transistor is not zero, four coefficients are needed
to describe its behaviour. We know that two of these
coefficients can be obtained from one set of characteristic
curves (e.g. the valve characteristics $i_a = f(U_g)$, with U_A as
parameter). To determine the four transistor coefficients,
however, at least two sets of characteristics are needed.

In the transistor, the variables are three voltages and three
currents, which are shown in *Figure 32* for a *p–n–p*-transistor,
with symbols and directions. But two of these six variables are
not independent of each other. For the voltages we have:
$U_{CE} = U_{CB} + U_{BE}$; and for the currents, Kirchhoff's law,
$I_E + I_B + I_C = 0$; which again means that four coefficients are

needed to determine the electrical behaviour of the transistor. The six coefficients can be abscissa, ordinate or parameter, as we like, and in this way we can draw 54 different sets of

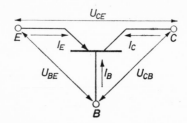

Figure 32. Transistor voltages and currents

characteristics. Which two of these are picked out to determine the four coefficients depends on the circumstances. For example, the current in the output circuit can be drawn as a function of the output voltage, once for constant input current and once for constant input voltage. If we choose these two sets of characteristics, we can draw two on one diagram, since they differ only in their parameter. This has been done in *Figure 33a–c* for the three modes of connection of an *n–p–n-*transistor, as follows:

Grounded-emitter circuit:

$$I_C = f(U_{CE}); \text{ parameters, } I_B \text{ and } U_{BE} \qquad \dots (9.1a)$$

Grounded-base circuit:

$$I_C = f(U_{CE}); \text{ parameters, } I_E \text{ and } U_{BE} \qquad \dots (9.1b)$$

Grounded-collector circuit:

$$I_E = f(U_{CE}); \text{ parameters, } I_B \text{ and } U_{CB} \qquad \dots (9.1c)$$

Generally, the four transistor coefficients of most interest are: the input resistance, the output resistance, the current amplification factor, and the voltage feedback factor.

These coefficients are closely related to the four-pole net-

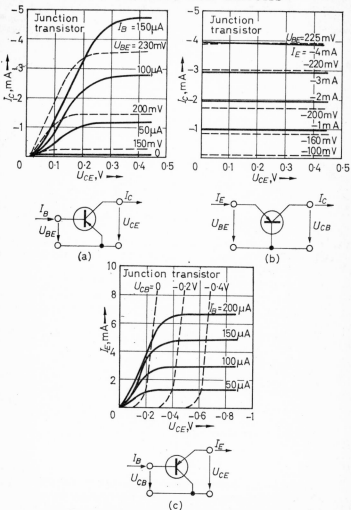

Figure 33. *Pairs of sets of characteristics:* (a) *Grounded emitter;* (b) *Grounded base;* (c) *Grounded collector*

(After Beneking)

work parameters of the transistor. This is discussed in Chapter 10.

In circuits, transistors are generally grounded-emitter or grounded-base. In both connections a relatively high input resistance is combined with a high output resistance, whereas in a grounded-collector circuit the input resistance is very high and the output resistance very low. We shall now describe a few basic circuits.

First look at the circuit of a transistor used as an amplifier. Here coupling by transformers is preferred, as this makes it

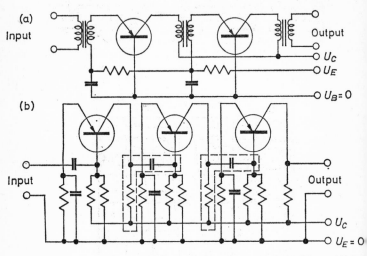

Figure 34. Transistor amplifiers: (a) Low-frequency amplifier with transformer coupling, grounded-base circuit; (b) RC-coupled amplifier, grounded-emitter connection (RC elements enclosed in dotted lines)

easier to match up with the input and output resistances of the transistor. *Figure 34a* shows a low-frequency amplification circuit with transformer coupling—the transistors are base grounded. *Figure 34b* shows a low-frequency amplifier with RC coupling, using grounded-emitter transistors.

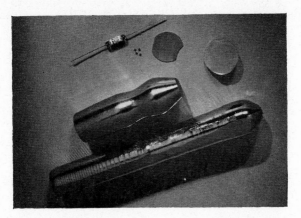

Plate 5. Ge single crystals at various stages of working

(After Hühn, C. F., *Telefunken-Z.*, 1958, **31,** No. 119)

Plate 6. The zone melting process, with no crucible (vertical, Si)

(After Goorissen, J., *Philips Techn. Rundschau*, 1959–60, **21,** No. 7)

Plate 7. Size comparison between present-day and micro-modular methods of construction: (a) New technique; (b) Old technique

[After Assmann, E., *Siemens–Z.*, 1960, 34 (11)]

Two simple oscillating circuits, in which transistors are used as transmitters, are given in *Figure 35a* and *b*. The transmitter shown in *Figure 35b* is particularly suitable for a portable apparatus. It can be compressed into a very small space and can, for example, be used for loudspeaker equipment, if the speaker does not require a firm support.

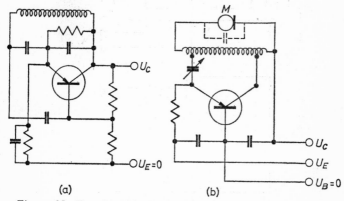

(a)   (b)

Figure 35. Transistor oscillators: (a) Colpitt circuit (grounded-emitter oscillator); (b) Small oscillator, after Toussaint (grounded-base oscillator, M—condenser microphone)

Transistors are highly suitable for building push–pull circuits because the second transistor can complement the first, i.e. if the first is an *n–p–n*-transistor the second can be *p–n–p*. This avoids the need for a voltage source such as push–pull valve circuits need. The circuit diagram (*Figure 36a*) shows that the transistor push–pull circuit needs only a few components, and is thus simpler than any circuit which could be made with thermionic valves. The way in which the push–pull amplifier works is very easy to see. In the steady state, that is, with no control current passing, the battery current flows to the base of both transistors, a small fraction to one, to bring it up to the base current of the other transistor, and a larger fraction which connects with the circuit via the collectors. A control current will reduce the base current of one transistor

H

101

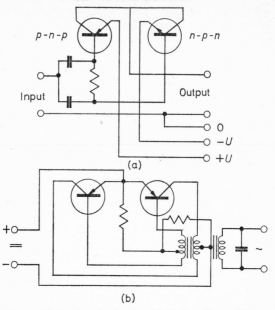

Figure 36. Push–pull circuits: (a) Push–pull amplifier;
(b) d.c.–a.c. converter

and increase that of the other. In this way the collector currents of the two transistors will be affected in opposite senses; the difference between the two collector currents will then flow in the output circuit. This utilizes the current-amplifying effect of two transistors. In building push–pull stages, it is necessary to have available *n–p–n-* and *p–n–p-* transistors with similar characteristics. In practice, however, it is very difficult to find two transistors which match, particularly when the characteristics still have to match at different temperatures.

Figure 36b shows a push–pull oscillator circuit with two *n–p–n-*transistors; it acts as a d.c.–a.c. converter. Controlled by the time constant of the impedance of the circuit, the two transistors alternately block the passage of current. As a

102

result, the currents from the transistor collectors flow in alternate directions through the middle transmitter winding. This induces an alternating current in the transmitter winding lying in the outer circuit.

Transistors are also popular as regulating devices in voltage stabilizing circuits in conjunction with semiconductor diodes, particularly Zener diodes. A simple circuit of this type and an arrangement for current limitation are shown in *Figure 37a* and *b*. In the voltage stabilizer the reference voltage—the value at which the voltage is to be stabilized—is determined by the Zener voltage U_z of the diode. The difference, as tapped off by the chain of resistors, between the actual voltage and its nominal value is amplified by the first transistor, whose collector current controls the second transistor, connected as a current restricter. Both transistors have grounded base. In *Figure 37b* the part of the stabilizing circuit which acts as current limiter is shown in a somewhat different form. Instead of a resistance, it has a diode in the forward direction in the collector circuit. This prevents the transistor from being overloaded. Such current limiters are used to protect transistorized instruments, because fuses or automatic safety devices do not generally cut out quickly enough to protect the semiconducting elements from damage.

Bistable switch (flip-flop) circuits with transistors have achieved great importance in electronic calculators. *Figure 38* is a circuit diagram of such a flip-flop stage. The circuit has two stable states, between which it can be switched backwards and forwards by pulses. The output is a series of pulses in a ratio of 2 (binary) to the input series. A series of flip-flop stages can be used to reproduce electronically the binary system of counting.

In the decimal system of counting, the position of a digit represents a power of ten, i.e. the value 10^0, 10^1, 10^2, 10^3, ... 10^{n-1}, according to whether the digit is in 1st, 2nd, 3rd, 4th, ... nth place before the decimal point. In the binary system the position of the digit similarly corresponds to 2^0, 2^1, 2^2, 2^3, ... 2^{n-1}. Since there are only two digits in the binary system, we can represent them by the symbols L and 0. For example, a number written in the binary

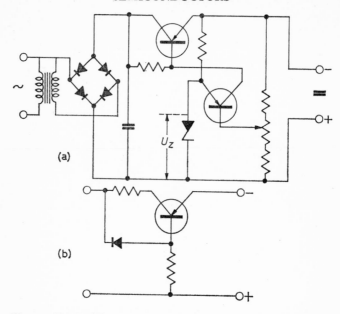

*Figure 37. Stabilizer circuits: (a) Mains stabilizing circuit;
(b) Current-limiting circuit element*

system may look like $L0LL0$. This is equivalent to
$1 \times 2^4 + 0 \times 2^3 + 1 \times 2^2 + 1 \times 2^1 + 0 \times 2^0 = 22$.

The binary system can be represented, for example, by
associating each output transistor of the flip-flop series with
a visual signal. Then the appearance of the visual signal
means the binary number L, and the absence of the signal
means the binary number 0.

Flip-flop circuits were first used as scaling circuits for
measuring quantities of radiation with counter tubes. Gas-
filled valves (thyratrons) were then used, but the instruments
were very expensive. The production of bistable switching
stages of this sort from space-saving transistor circuits
helped to open the way to the many applications of today.

Calculating on the binary system requires, in addition,

that $0+0=0$, $L+0=L$, $0+L=L$, and $L+L=0$, with L (in the last case) carried to the next higher place. Circuit elements which can reproduce these relationships electronically are therefore needed. Two circuits have been found sufficient, and from these two combinations can be made to

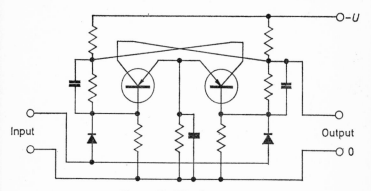

Figure 38. Flip-flop circuit

carry out all the logical operations needed in electronic calculations. They are the series and parallel circuits of two transistors, which correspond to the logical relations 'neither/nor' and 'both/and' (*Figure 39a* and *b*). When in series, one of the two transistors acts as a barrier when one of the two inputs receives a pulse L. When in parallel, on the other hand, both inputs must receive a pulse L in order to make both transistors act as barriers. In the first case, only with a combination will there be an output pulse (L), whereas in the second case, only with a combination will there be no output pulse (0). This circuit technique, whose essential components are resistors (R), condensers (C) and transistors (T), is called an *RCT* technique. It has become customary to work with a simplified system of circuit symbols. This is used in *Figure 39a* and *b*. With the aid of these symbols, all the circuits used in (digital) computers working on the binary system can be represented in simplified form. *Figure 39c* shows the flip-flop circuit using this symbolism. Such types of combinations of switches are called gates. In the field of electronic computing, flip-flop gates also represent time-dependent functions, because one

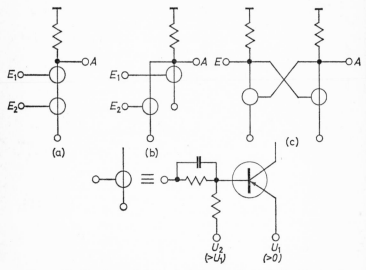

*Figure 39. Circuit symbols for logical operations: (a) 'neither/nor';
(b) 'both/and'; (c) Flip-flop storage element*

pulse is sometimes suppressed by the other, thus enabling the passage of time to be reckoned. At the same time the flip-flop gate represents the simplest form of storage, such as is required when working with data.

Automatic calculating from given data by the binary system in electronic (digital) computers by means of the pulse technique has acquired great importance because Wiener, in 1948, succeeded in establishing an inverse Fourier integral relationship which—just as the Fourier integral of discontinuous functions leads back to a continuous system of functions—enables continuous functions to be represented by means of discontinuous functions (step functions,

Dirac's δ-function). This illustrates the fundamental equivalence of the continuous and discontinuous mode of representation, as reflected in physics by the simultaneous existence of the wave and particle hypotheses, and enables a continuous infinity to be converted into an infinity capable of being counted. In this way the continuum is also made accessible to mathematical statistics and has led to another branch of science, to which Wiener has given the name cybernetics, but which is also often known as information theory, because it has found its most successful application in this field.

The representation of functions by step functions can be carried out electronically. The step functions are formed by pulses, i.e. by binary steps: either there is a pulse, L, or there is no pulse, 0. Since in British and American literature this binary step is known as a *b*inary dig*it*, the number of binary decisions is counted in units known as 'bits'. This formation of step functions by pulse techniques, together with the binary computing method by means of the circuit elements described above (*Figure 39a–c*), form the basis of the wide range of applications of digital computers.

We have already mentioned above (p. 106) the problem of the storage of pulses, which is of great importance in computers for operating on given data. Besides the method mentioned, of storage in groups of transistor flip-flop circuits, a series of magnetic storage methods (magnetic drums, magnetic tapes, ferrite cores) has also been developed, so that the storage capacity and speed of computers are now of the same order as, and sometimes even surpass, the capacities for storing and speeds of communicating information known to us in the biological field. Table 7 gives the rates of information or storage in bit/sec for men and machines.

Table 7. Information and Storage Rates (after Küpfmüller)

	Data (*bit/sec*)		
	Calculating	*Image*	*Sound*
Man	3–5	2×10^7	$3{\cdot}5 \times 10^4$
Machine	10^4	$1{\cdot}3 \times 10^7$	$3{\cdot}0 \times 10^4$

SEMICONDUCTORS

We see that computers are superior to the human brain as regards the information rate in calculating, and about equally good for images and sound. But they have not nearly the brain's capacity for storing information. The storage capacity of the brain, at 10^{15} bits, is still about 10^9 times that of a machine. It is approximately proportional to the number of switch elements, whose function in the biological field is assumed by the nerve cells (neurons).

10

THE TRANSISTOR AS A FOUR-TERMINAL NETWORK

THE symbols used in circuit diagrams for the three ways of connecting a transistor (grounded emitter, grounded base and grounded collector) in *Figures 16* and *33a–c* (pp. 67 and 99) show that the transistor may also be considered as a four-terminal network. It is an active network, because it possesses amplifying properties. It is unsymmetrical, because it consists of regions having different types of conduction, separated by junctions where the conductivity is directional. Strictly speaking, it is not a linear network, because its conductance depends on frequency as soon as the limiting frequency, determined by the width of the base and by the life and mean free path of the charge carriers, is exceeded. But we shall confine ourselves to describing processes occurring at frequencies below the critical value, so that the four-terminal network may be assumed to be linear.

As we know, the four-terminal network equations can be expressed in many different ways to connect the input coefficients (U_1, I_1) with the output coefficients (U_2, I_2); and for the case of the transistor we have various voltages and currents available (U_{BC}, U_{CE}, U_{EB}, or I_B, I_C, I_E), depending on the method of connection. Once again, the choice of equation is of course governed by the purpose of the calculations, just as the choice of sets of characteristics (*see* p. 97). This time the aim is to get the simplest possible relations between the data in which we are interested (*see* p. 98) and the network parameters. We therefore start with the functional relations $U_1 = f(I_1, U_2)$ and $I_2 = g(I_1, U_2)$ and assume that any changes in currents and voltages ($\Delta U_1 = u_1$ or $\Delta I_2 = i_2$) are small. We can then assume a linear relation between these changes and write:

$$u_1 = \left(\frac{\partial U_1}{\partial I_1}\right)_{U_2} i_1 + \left(\frac{\partial U_1}{\partial U_2}\right)_{I_1} u_2 \qquad \ldots (10.1a)$$

$$i_2 = \left(\frac{\partial I_2}{\partial I_1}\right)_{U_2} i_1 + \left(\frac{\partial I_2}{\partial U_2}\right)_{I_1} u_2 \qquad \ldots (10.1b)$$

with the network parameters:

Short-circuit input resistance:

$$h_{11} = \left(\frac{u_1}{i_1}\right)_{u_2=0} = \left(\frac{\partial U_1}{\partial I_1}\right)_{U_2} \qquad \ldots (10.1c)$$

Short-circuit current amplification:

$$h_{21} = \left(\frac{i_2}{i_1}\right)_{u_2=0} = \left(\frac{\partial I_2}{\partial I_1}\right)_{U_2} \qquad \ldots (10.1d)$$

No-load feedback voltage:

$$h_{12} = \left(\frac{u_1}{u_2}\right)_{i_1=0} = \left(\frac{\partial U_1}{\partial U_2}\right)_{I_1} \qquad \ldots (10.1e)$$

No-load output conductance:

$$h_{22} = \left(\frac{i_2}{u_2}\right)_{i_1=0} = \left(\frac{\partial I_2}{\partial U_2}\right)_{I_1} \qquad \ldots (10.1f)$$

obtained by putting first $i_1=0$ (i.e. $I_1=$ constant) and then $u_2=0$ (i.e. $U_2=$ constant) in equations 10.1a, b. In fact, this choice of network equations enables the important, physically significant data to be obtained directly as network parameters (of which h_{22} is the reciprocal of the no-load output resistance). The current amplification factor of the grounded-base mode of connection is usually denoted by α. We then have:

$$|h_{21b}| = \alpha \qquad \ldots (10.2a)$$

FOUR-TERMINAL NETWORK

The short-circuit input resistance can be obtained approximately for the grounded-base connection. For between the emitter and the base there is only the diffusion potential difference $U_T = 0.025$ V (*see* p. 15, but for $T = 273°K$) which enables the emitter current I_E to flow. Since the emitter current is of the order of 1 mA, we may put:

$$h_{11b} = 25 \, \Omega \qquad \qquad \text{.... (10.2b)}$$

The network parameters can be determined graphically from the sets of characteristics, in the same way as the internal resistance, slope (and inverse amplification factor) of a thermionic valve are determined graphically. As an example, we may take four sets of characteristics for the grounded-emitter connection (*Figure 40a–d*). By drawing through the working point the straight lines corresponding to constant values of the abscissa and ordinate, we get the values of u and i, as the distances from the neighbouring curve in the set, and their quotient gives the required value of h.

Network parameters with a physical interpretation which can have practical application can also be obtained by putting the network equations into the following form:

$$i_1 = y_{11}u_1 + y_{12}u_2 \qquad \text{.... (10.3a)}$$

$$i_2 = y_{21}u_1 + y_{22}u_2 \qquad \text{.... (10.3b)}$$

where:

the short-circuit input conductance $y_{11} = \left(\dfrac{i_1}{u_1}\right)_{u_2=0}$

the forward slope $y_{21} = \left(\dfrac{i_2}{u_1}\right)_{u_2=0}$

the reverse slope $y_{12} = \left(\dfrac{i_1}{u_2}\right)_{u_2=0}$ and

the short-circuit output conductance $y_{22} = \left(\dfrac{i_2}{u_2}\right)_{u_1=0}$

The network parameters in the two systems of equations 10.1 and 10.3 can be interconverted according to the rules of the theory of determinants.

Under some circumstances the description of the electrical behaviour of a transistor can be reduced to fewer than four

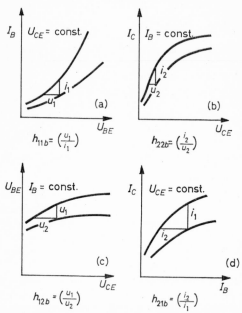

$$h_{11b} = \left(\frac{u_1}{i_1}\right)$$

$$h_{22b} = \left(\frac{i_2}{u_2}\right)$$

$$h_{12b} = \left(\frac{u_1}{u_2}\right)$$

$$h_{21b} = \left(\frac{i_2}{i_1}\right)$$

Figure 40. Sets of characteristics (diagrammatic) for the graphical determination of the parameter h in grounded-emitter circuits: (a) h_{11b}; (b) h_{22b}; (c) h_{12b}; (d) h_{21b}

coefficients; in a very extreme case, to the most important parameter, the current amplification $\alpha = |h_{21b}|$. This is the case for a grounded-base transistor when the load resistance in the output circuit is very much smaller than the no-load output resistance $(1/h_{22b})$. We can then put $u_2 \approx 0$ and therefore, from equation 10.1b, $i_2 = h_{21b}i_1$. The short-circuit input resistance h_{11b} in equation 10.1a can in general be considered as known for the grounded-base circuit, from equation 10.2b.

After the successful description of the behaviour of the

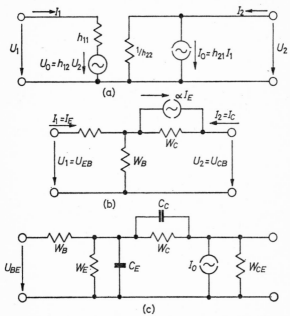

Figure 41. Equivalent circuit diagrams for the transistor: (a) For low frequencies with h parameters (U_0—source of primary voltage, I_0—source of primary current); (b) For grounded-base circuits (T-circuit element: W_B—resistance of base, W_C—resistance of collector); (c) For grounded-emitter circuits, after Giacoletto (π-circuit element: C_E—capacity of emitter, C_C—capacity of collector, W_{CE}—leak resistance between emitter and collector)

transistor by the four-terminal network theory, a further success was achieved, by various ways and means, in describing the action and function of the transistor with equivalent circuit diagrams. *Figure 41a* gives a complete equivalent circuit valid for low frequencies (below the critical frequency), and explains the functions of the four-pole parameters h_{ik}. *Figure 41b* and *c* are equivalent circuits deduced from this: an equivalent T circuit for the grounded-base connection and an equivalent π circuit for the grounded emitter. This latter was first given by Giacoletto and is often used. It takes account of the capacitances, leak resistances and series resistances between the three electrodes of a transistor, and represents the activity of the network by inserting a primary source of current between the emitter and collector, with a view to reproducing the relationships in the grounded-emitter circuit.

11

SPECIFIC APPLICATIONS

SEMICONDUCTORS with electronic conduction have properties differing from those of metals which make them particularly suitable for certain applications. These properties are most easily understood with the aid of the band model of the electrons, according to which they are due to the existence of bands of energies which electrons are permitted to occupy and which are separated from each other by forbidden zones: in particular, the existence of the valence band and the conduction band, which are separated by the first forbidden zone, of bandwidth ΔE, largely accounts, as shown in the preceding chapters, for the descriptions of the observed phenomena. The variable width of the forbidden zone, and the curvature of the edges of the bands which this causes, may be attributed to the existence of some extremely high electron and hole mobilities (*see* p. 76), observed particularly in indium antimonide and indium arsenide. This is especially noticeable in the behaviour of these substances in a magnetic field, which causes considerable changes in resistance (*see* Table 4, pp. 74–75). Semiconductors show such large electromagnetic effects that they have found practical application in the Hall generator and the electromagnetic amplifier. Their high thermoelectric power (Seebeck coefficient) which may attain the highest theoretical value possible from equation 3.6d, is found in compounds and alloys of lead with S, Se and Te in conjunction with a high thermal conductivity (*see* p. 77), which enables these to be used in thermoelectric cooling processes. The possibility of also filling up higher bands of permitted energies with electrons by means of higher energies of excitation enables the process of recombination to take place in two stages, with the second stage consisting in the simultaneous recombination of a larger number of electrons, so that a coherent electromagnetic radiation is emitted whose electromagnetic power can be put to practical use. This process is now known by the name of 'maser', an abbreviation of 'microwave amplification by stimulated radiation'. Very recently, the same process has also been extended to the amplification of light intensities (laser: 'light' instead of 'microwave').

Another specific application, which is based on the fact that the thickness of a junction varies with the reverse voltage in p–n-junctions (see p. 57), is the application of semiconductor components to parametric amplification. Finally, by means of semiconductors, mechanical energy can be converted into electrical energy, using their piezoelectric properties. We have already discussed their uses as spectrographic filters (p. 78), and will now discuss in more detail five of the specific applications mentioned above: the Hall generator, the electromagnetic amplifier, thermoelectric cooling, the production of microwaves (maser) and parametric amplification.

The Hall Generator

The Hall effect, in which a magnetic field produces a Hall voltage U_H at the edges of a conductor and at right angles to the direction of the current (see p. 20, Table 1, and p. 8), may be utilized to produce a Hall output in the Hall generator, which employs the semiconductors InSb and InAs, which have high electron mobilities and show a considerable Hall effect, big enough to be put to practical use.

For the Hall voltage U_H we may put, from Table 1,

$$U_H = R_H \frac{I}{d} B = \frac{I}{end} B \qquad \ldots\ldots (11.1a)$$

in which we have used equation 2.4, putting d for the thickness of the semiconductor and B for the induction of the magnetic field H. Instead of the current density j_e we have used the current strength $I = j_e bd$ (b = width of semiconductor).

116

Figure 42 shows the principal connections for a **Hall** generator. The Hall voltage U_H is proportional both to the primary current I and to the magnetic induction B (*see* Table 1), and is thus a measure of the product of these quantities. The Hall generator is therefore suitable for the

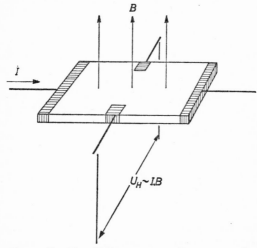

Figure 42. The Hall generator: diagram of the mode of operation

measurement of torques in d.c. machines, by inserting a narrow semiconductor into the gap between the pole piece and the armature and allowing part of the armature current to flow through the semiconductor as primary current, which gives rise to a Hall voltage proportional to the product of the magnetic induction and the armature current. In this way the Hall generator can govern a regulator which prevents the machine being overloaded. Another use is as an output meter. The primary current must then be chosen to be proportional to the consumer current, and the magnetic induction proportional to the consumer voltage (or vice versa). If the primary current is kept constant, the Hall generator may also

117

be used to measure the strength of the magnetic induction or magnetic field. Kuhrt has recently used thin plates of semiconductor ($1 \times 2 \times 0 \cdot 3$ mm) as Hall probes between plates of ferrite as a pick-up head in a tape recorder (*Figure 43*).

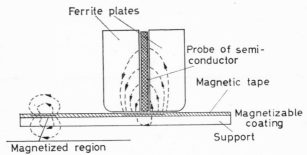

Figure 43. The Hall generator: pick-up head for the symbols on magnetic tape

The magnetic flux of the tape in the region where the pick-up head is placed is caused by the ferrite plates to flow perpendicularly through the layer of semiconductor, so that between the top and bottom edges of the semiconducting plate there will be a Hall voltage proportional to the magnetization of the tape if a constant current flows through the semiconductor perpendicular to the plane of the diagram. With the Hall probe, unlike the inductive method of pick-up, the symbols on the magnetic tape can also be picked up when the tape is at rest; a very important feature, for instance, in the magnetic storage of information (*see* p. 107).

Some idea of the output of Hall generators can be gained from the following considerations. The primary current I may be considered as the product of the conductivity of the semiconductor $\sigma = en\mu_n$ and the strength of the electric field $|\mathfrak{E}| = U_H/l$ (where l is the length of the semiconductor), so that for a cross-section bd:

$$I = en\mu_n U \frac{bd}{l} \qquad \dots \text{(11.1b)}$$

In conjunction with equation 11.1a, this gives:

$$U_H = U \frac{b}{l} \mu_n B \qquad \qquad \dots (11.1c)$$

The Hall power N_H is then given by:

$$N_H = \frac{U_H^2}{R_E} = \frac{U^2}{R_E} \frac{b^2}{l^2} \mu_n^2 B^2 \qquad \dots (11.1d)$$

where R_E is the resistance of the semiconductor between the Hall electrodes. Equation 11.1d tells us the important fact that the Hall power is proportional to the square of the mobility of the electrons. Since μ_n for InSb and InAs is about 10 times as high as for Ge, the Hall power of the two $A^{III}B^V$ compounds is about 10 times as great as that of Ge. This Hall power will heat up the semiconductor, so that semiconductors with a lower temperature coefficient of conductance —i.e. having a low intrinsic conduction due to a wide forbidden zone—are more suitable for constructing Hall generators. Table 4 (pp. 74–75) shows that InAs is superior to InSb in this respect.

The high Hall power of the two $A^{III}B^V$ compounds suggested to Weiss that the output from a Hall generator might be fed back to produce oscillations. *Figure 44* is a diagram of such a circuit, in which the Hall circuit and the primary circuit are inductively coupled by an iron core, and the semiconductor lies in the magnetic field of a gap in this core.

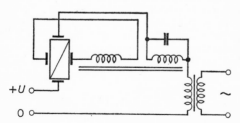

Figure 44. Feedback circuit for producing oscillations

SEMICONDUCTORS

Electromagnetic Amplifier

The Hall generator represents the practical application of the transverse electric electromagnetic effect, and the electromagnetic amplifier represents an application of the corresponding longitudinal effect, the Thomson effect, which consists in a change in resistance in a magnetic field (Table 1). Before the particular electromagnetic properties of the $A^{III}B^V$ compounds were known, bismuth (Bi) was used by Lenard to measure the strength of magnetic fields by means of its change in resistance (see p. 19), but InSb is about 40 times as good as Bi for this purpose. The resistance effect is, however, not only a property of the material but depends on the geometry of the element, which affects the paths of the current (the paths of the charge carriers). The simplest geometrical parameter is the length of a conductor, for which reason Lenard used a spiral of Bi to measure a magnetic field. The best shape, however, is the Corbino disc (*Figure 45a*), in which the edge forms an equipotential surface, leads are connected to the edge and to the middle of the disc, and the charge carriers move along spiral paths. The particular electrical property of the edge prevents potential differences from arising, and thus avoids the Hall effect, which in this case would be a disturbing factor. The behaviour of ρ_B/ρ_0 for InSb has been plotted by Welker in *Figure 45b* for various shapes of semiconductor. If, for example, a thin Corbino disc C of InSb is placed in the narrow gap of an electromagnet (*Figure 45c*), a considerable change ΔI in the current I flowing through the semiconductor can be produced by a weak control current I_{st}, and an amplification of about a thousand times can be achieved. As can be shown, $\Delta\rho/\rho$ is also proportional to the square of the electron mobility μ_n, so that the semiconductors InSb and InAs are just as good for building electromagnetic amplifiers as for Hall generators.

Thermoelectric Cooling

In discussing thermoelectric phenomena (p. 24), we deduced an equation (3.6b) connecting the maximum reduction in temperature ΔT which can be achieved by means of the Peltier effect, the thermoelectric figure of merit $Z = \alpha^2\sigma/\kappa$

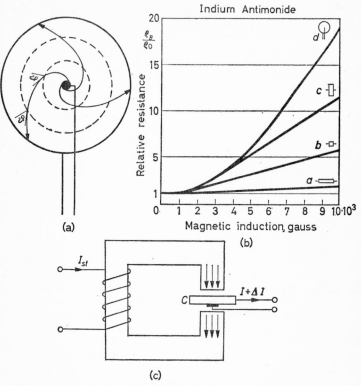

Figure 45. Applications of the Thomson effect: (a) Corbino disc; (b) ρ_B/ρ_0 for InSb as a function of its geometry; (c) Electromagnetic amplifier

(*see* p. 77) and the temperature of the surroundings. Since Z is proportional to the square of the thermoelectric power α, it is possible, by means of semiconductors, which in general have high values of α (*see* Table 4), to achieve a cooling effect big enough to be of practical value. For example, with a value of $Z = 2.10^{-3}$, which we can take as an average for usable semiconductors—the highest values of Z yet reached are about 5.10^{-3}—and surroundings at a temperature of $T = 300°$ K, a reduction in temperature of $90°$ can be achieved under favourable conditions. As a rule, however, we have to be content with only a fraction (about 30 per cent) of this amount, because the optimum conditions to which equation 3.6b applies the Seebeck effect, which appears as a reaction and is the opposite of the Peltier effect, balanced out by the conduction of heat, are not strictly fulfilled.

The plan of construction of a thermal battery for cooling purposes proposed by Ioffé is shown in *Figure 46a*. The thermal battery consists of a block of three thermocouples in

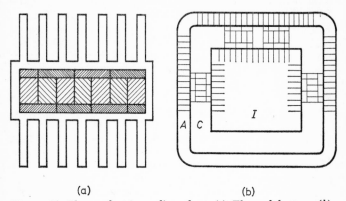

(a)   (b)

Figure 46. Thermoelectric cooling plant: (a) Thermal battery; (b) Refrigerator (diagrammatic) (I—interior, C—cooling jacket with thermal batteries, A—heat exchange with the outside by cooling fins)

series, one element (*n*-conducting) of each couple being made of an alloy of PbSe and PbTe and the other element (*p*-conducting) of one with Sb and Te as its main components. The blocks formed by the elements are made by sintering the powdered substances at $400°$ C under a pressure of 4,000–6,000 kg/cm². Connecting the separate elements of the thermocouples is still a difficult technical problem. The connecting material must fulfil several stringent conditions. It must have good electrical and thermal conductivity; the internal contact which it makes with the thermocouple elements must have negligible electrical and thermal contact resistance, and, with these strict electrical and thermal requirements, it must not be subject to atmospheric corrosion nor liable to alter under mechanical stresses, such as the tensile and compressive stresses resulting from the difference in temperature between the hot and cold contact plates of the battery. With copper plates forming the connection, an alloy of 80 per cent Bi and 20 per cent Sn, which makes good contact, has proved serviceable for soldering the copper plates and the blocks of thermocouple elements at 200° C. The thermal battery is provided with heat-exchanger fins on both sides, which remove the heat of the hot contact plates and disperse it to the surroundings, and pass on the coldness of the cold contact plates to the space which it is desired to cool. Thermal batteries of the type described can be used for building refrigerators, as can be seen in *Figure 46b*. According to Ioffé, with a consumption of 75 W it is possible to maintain a temperature of between 0 and −5° C in a 40 l. thermoelectric refrigerator of this type with an outside temperature of 22° C (295° K).

The advantages of the thermoelectric cooling process over other methods of cooling are undoubtedly its simplicity—the absence of any movable parts or moving liquids or gases—as well as its life, which in theory is unlimited. But before such refrigerators can be produced on a large scale, the technical difficulties mentioned, of making non-corrosive and mechanically insensitive contacts, have to be overcome. For small amounts of cooling, however, the thermoelectric method is already in frequent use: in meteorology, for example, in dew-point measurement, as a cooling column in vacuum technique or in microscopy for cooling the objects observed.

At the moment the use of semiconductor thermocouples to produce electrical energy (thermoelectric generators) is also of some interest, because in nuclear reactions we have available an almost inexhaustible source of heat energy. To reach higher voltages, however, it is still necessary to connect a number of thermocouples in series, with all the disadvantages this entails (increase in the internal resistance and in the number of contact faces). According to Ioffé, a thermoelectric generator has been developed which uses the hot combustion gases from an oil lamp as a source of current for a transistorized radio receiver or transistorized telephone exchange. Thermoelectric generators have also been used with advantage to regulate thermostats and as solar batteries.

Microwave Oscillator (Maser)—Molecular Amplifier

The possibility of utilizing the passage of electrons, in semiconducting substances, from the valence band or a donor energy level to the conduction band and other higher energy levels, separated from each other by more forbidden zones— i.e. controlled two-stage and multi-stage processes (*see* p. 51) —forms the basis for the amplification of microwaves by coherent electron transitions, or, under conditions favourable for growth, for the production of microwaves.

As a rule a three-stage process (*Figure 47a*) is used. By an alternating magnetic field of frequency ν_{13} (pumping frequency) energy is added to the electrons in energy level 1 by gyromagnetic resonance with the electron spin, so that their energy level rises to 3 ($\Delta E = h\nu_{13}$). The number of electrons in this level is then far greater than would correspond to thermal equilibrium according to the Boltzmann distribution (3.5f), so that the state of distribution, calculated from equation 3.5f, would correspond to a negative absolute temperature. This accumulation of electrons serves as a reservoir for energy level 2, which is occupied by normal thermal electrons; as soon as the thermal equilibrium in 2 is disturbed, electrons from 3 fall down to 2. A low-energy radiation of frequency ν_{12} (signal frequency) can disturb this equilibrium and enable electrons to jump simultaneously (coherently) from 2 to 1. This amplifies the radiation, or wave, having the signal frequency ν_{12}, or, under favourable growth conditions, produces a radiation of frequency ν_{12}. Meanwhile, energy level 2 continues to be filled up from energy level 3, while the wave having the pumping frequency ν_{13} keeps the reservoir (energy level 3) stocked. Here it is important that the lengths of time (τ_{ik}) which the electrons spend in the

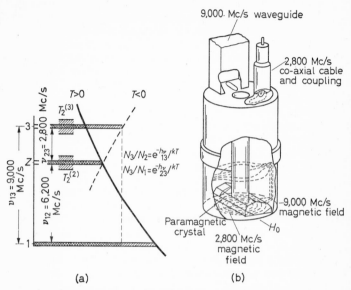

Figure 47. Molecular amplifier (maser): (a) Bands occupied with electrons in non-thermal equilibrium; (b) Design for a maser by Rothe

energy levels, and the probabilities of transitions of electrons between them, which depend on temperature, shall be suitably related to each other. For this three-stage process, therefore, with signal frequency ν_{12}, we must have:

$$\tau_{31} \gg \tau_{21} \quad \text{and} \quad \tau_{32} \ll \tau_{21} \qquad \ldots . (11.2a)$$

if electrons are to accumulate in energy levels 1 and 2.

But a three-stage process can also take place when ν_{23} is the signal frequency. Then there must be a different relationship between the τ, viz.:

$$\tau_{31} \gg \tau_{21} \quad \text{and} \quad \tau_{21} \ll \tau_{32} \qquad \ldots . (11.2b)$$

so that energy level 2 is always able to receive more electrons from energy level 3.

SEMICONDUCTORS

A semiconductor which is suitable for putting the first of these three-stage processes into practice is crystallized lanthanum ethyl sulphate, $La\,(C_2H_5SO_4)_3.9H_2O$, into the lattice of which gadolinium impurity centres have been introduced. For this substance the frequencies have the following values: pumping frequency $\nu_{13} = 17\cdot5$ Gc/s; signal frequency $\nu_{12} = 9$ Gc/s; transition frequency $\nu_{23} = 8\cdot5$ Gc/s.

For the second three-stage process, chromium atoms as impurity centres in Al_2O_3 (ruby) or in $K_3CO(CN)_6$ (cobalt potassium cyanide) are suitable. The appropriate frequency values are then: pumping frequency $\nu_{13} = 9$ Gc/s; signal frequency $\nu_{23} = 2\cdot86$ Gc/s; transition frequency $\nu_{12} = 6\cdot2$ Gc/s.

The experimental realization of this process requires a resonator (cavity) with two resonant frequencies, corresponding to the pumping frequency and signal frequency (*Figure 47b*). Another difficulty is that the signal wave entering a molecular amplifier is reflected back amplified along the same conductor (a dipole—in *Figure 47b* a coaxial cable) by which it enters, and only after this can it be separated electronically into an input and an output (four-terminal network). To do this a device called a circulator is employed.

The circulator is constructed from waveguides built of directional conductors (isolators) (*Figure 48a*). In the form shown in the diagram, a premagnetized ferrite rod is built into the waveguide. A wave coming from the left of the diagram is rotated in a direction corresponding to the elementary magnets in the ferrite and is scarcely damped at all, but one coming into the isolator from the right is moving against the spin and is heavily damped.

The circulator is constructed of four isolators of this type connected as a bridge (*Figure 48b*). The input and output of the molecular amplifier are then cleanly separated, while a resistor (Z_0) ensures that the power reflected from the receiver input is absorbed.

The amplification and production of microwaves by the maser does not make use of any thermally-stimulated electrons; on the contrary, the value of the frequency is so adjusted that the thermal lives of the electrons are always greater than the period of oscillations at the pumping frequency and signal frequency, i.e. at no time is the material in a state of thermal equilibrium. The maser is therefore largely free from noise, except for a very slight noise arising from spontaneous emission (probably due to cosmic rays). This corresponds to emission at 2° K. Unfortunately these ideal low-noise con-

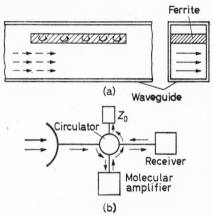

Figure 48. Directional waveguides: (a) Diagram of an isolator; (b) Principal circuit of a circulator

ditions cannot be fully utilized because of the thermal noise in the leads and accessory equipment. The low-noise conditions existing in the maser could only be achieved by extremely severe cooling of the circuit elements operating with thermal electrons.

The almost complete absence of thermal noise makes the maser very suitable for the amplification of very low powers $(10^{-28} \text{ W/cm}^2)$. It is therefore used primarily in radiotelescopes and enables radioastronomers to discover radio stars a very long way away, and tracking stations to maintain radio contact with artificial satellites moving at a great distance in space.

Parametric Amplification

Semiconductors have made possible the low-noise amplification and production of microwaves in the maser, and it

127

is a special property of semiconducting diodes, namely the fact that their capacitance (reactance) alters with the reverse voltage (p. 57), which has led to low-noise amplification based on a different principle. This is the principle of the child's swing; an increase in the amplitude of an oscillation by a push in the same direction at the end of each swing. For a corresponding electrical process, we require an oscillating circuit with a variable capacitance, e.g. a plate condenser in which the distance between the plates can be periodically increased and decreased. The condenser, of capacitance C, is given a charge Q at time $t = 0$ at a voltage U_0. If, still at time $t = 0$, the charged plates are quickly pulled apart, by doing work against the electrostatic forces of attraction, then the capacitance will decrease as a result of the increase in the distance between the plates, and the voltage will reach the value U_1 $(U_1 > U_0)$, because the charge Q is assumed to have remained unaltered. The condenser will then discharge itself across the oscillating circuit. At time $t = T/2$ ($T =$ period of oscillation) the voltage on the condenser will have reached the value zero. At this instant the plates (with no expenditure or gain of energy, because at this instant there is no charge on the condenser) are rapidly brought closer together. After one complete oscillation $(t = T)$, the voltage will have again reached its original value U_1. But now (by doing work) the condenser plates are pulled apart again, and the cycle is repeated with a new initial voltage U_2, where $U_2 > U_1$, and so on. In this way, in the case described mechanical energy is pumped into the electromagnetic circuit at twice the frequency of the oscillating circuit, and appears as an increase in electromagnetic energy which can be expressed, in the equivalent circuit diagram, as a periodically varying negative resistance. This type of amplification is called parametric, because it is achieved by varying one of the oscillator parameters, in this case the capacitance C. By stimulating the circuit in counter-phase (in the above example, by increasing the capacitance by bringing the condenser plates together at time $t = 0$), the opposite of amplification—damping —is achieved (comparable with stopping a swing by pushes in the opposite direction).

SPECIFIC APPLICATIONS

The mechanically varying condenser which we have employed to explain the principle of parametric amplification is in practice replaced by a semiconductor diode (varactor, or varistor). The circuit of such an amplifier is given in *Figure 49*. Just as in the molecular amplifier, we have to

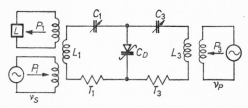

Figure 49. Circuit diagram of a parametric amplifier

distinguish between a pumping frequency ν_P and a signal frequency ν_S, where $\nu_P = 2\nu_S$, and to separate the input and output the dipole must once again be converted to a four-terminal network. In the parametric amplifier, too, this is most easily done by a circulator. The condition that the frequency ν_P should be strictly equal to $2\nu_S$ may be replaced by using an accessory circuit (dummy circuit) tuned to the difference frequency $(\nu_P - \nu_S)$.

12

THE FUTURE OUTLOOK

IT HAS been our task in the preceding chapters to report in simple terms on the present state of our knowledge of electronic semiconductors, and, from the position reached, we shall try to guess what progress may be expected in the near future. The development of semiconductor components appears to be proceeding along five main lines, namely: (1) higher critical frequencies; (2) greater thermal and photo-e.m.f.'s; (3) less noise; (4) smaller size; (5) further development of the laser.

These trends are stimulated by the many applications in the fields of computers, communications, remote control, rockets and control equipment. These all depend upon having available a series of high-frequency pulses from small, light but powerful current-economizing instruments to enable us to detect very small outputs and to save space and weight.

Considerable progress has recently been achieved in this last direction, and instruments now occupy between one-hundredth and one-thousandth of the space used hitherto.

In micromodular techniques, the size of semiconductor components, as well as the other elements required in circuits, e.g. resistors, coils and condensers, is tremendously reduced, and they are produced in a standard form of small—e.g. hexagonal—discs about 8 mm in diameter and about 1 mm thick (*Figure 50*). To make a circuit (e.g. a flip-flop stage) they are assembled into tiny prismatic blocks and set in plastic. By using a hexagonal shape a great deal of space can be saved, as *Plate 7* shows. Eight flip-flop stages take up less space than would one such circuit made from the separate elements as before.

A further step forward in combining the functions of circuit elements is molecular electronics or integrated circuitry. This

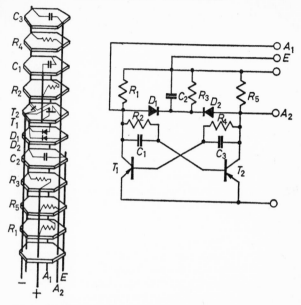

Figure 50. Construction of a micromodular flip-flop stage (diagrammatic)
[After Assmann, E., *Siemens-Z.*, 1960, 34(11)]

tries to combine the separate circuit elements in one single semiconductor crystal having a great many layers of different kinds of conductance, in a single 'functional block'. In this block, for instance, a condenser may be formed by two layers with good conduction separated by an insulating layer. If this layer is not insulating, but merely has a higher resistance than the adjacent layers, then the whole acts rather like a condenser with a resistance shunted across it. A resistance layer which heats a thermoelectrically active layer across an electrically insulating intermediate layer will work like a rectifier (*Figure 51a* and *b*). At present such a functional block cannot be made as a whole. It is still assembled from separate crystals. But all the same it takes up very little room,

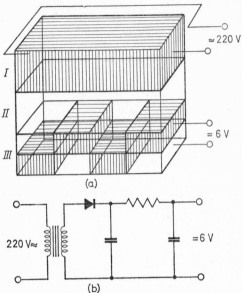

≈ 220 V

= 6 V

(a)

220 V≈   = 6 V

(b)

Figure 51. Rectifier functional block: (a) Diagram showing its structure; (b) Traditional circuit diagram

because germanium single crystals can now be made in the form of a strip 1·2 mm wide and a few μ thick (fir-tree crystals). Using these, a flip-flop stage, for instance, may be compressed into a plate 6·3 mm long, 3 mm wide and 0·76 mm thick (volume 14 mm³). Thirteen flip-flop stages take up 0·3 cm³ and weigh 1·5 g. As has already been mentioned, attempts are being made to compress the whole circuit into a single semiconducting crystal, and draw the finished functional block out of the melt. The first step has been taken in this direction, and single crystals of semiconductor have been made with five different layers (including the transition layers) by appropriate doping of the melt (*see* pp. 37, 82). This opens up a whole field of semiconductor technology, which will lead to the manufacture of functional blocks,

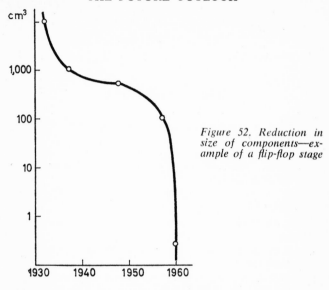

Figure 52. Reduction in size of components—example of a flip-flop stage

serving more and more purposes, directly from the molten basis substance, by doping in different ways. *Figure 52* shows the progress which has so far been made in saving space, using the example of the flip-flop circuit, which has been known for some 30 years.

Another new field of applications for semiconductors is opening up in opto-electronics. This is concerned with the coupling of photoresistors (CdS, CdSe) to electroluminescent cells, in which an electric field stimulates the substance to non-thermal luminescence. Low-power light (radiation) falling on a photoresistor can produce an output of electro-luminescent radiation 10 times as great (light amplification). This lays the foundations for the construction of new types of image amplifiers and converters (especially x-ray image converters) and methods of image storing.

K

BIBLIOGRAPHY

Smith, R. A. *Semiconductors.* 1959. London; Cambridge University Press

Ioffé, A. F. *Semiconductor Thermoelements and Thermoelectric Cooling.* Translated from Russian by A. Gelbtuch. 1958. London; Infosearch

Putley, E. H. *Hall Effect and Related Phenomena.* 1960. London; Butterworths

Lawson, W. D. and Nielson, S. *Preparation of Single Crystals.* 1958. London; Butterworths

Moss, T. S. *Optical Properties of Semi-conductors.* 1959. London; Butterworths

Wolfendale, E. *The Transistor.* 1963. London; Heywood

Shockley, W. *Electrons and Holes in Semiconductors.* 1953. New York; Van Nostrand

Dunlap, W. C., jun. *An Introduction to Semiconductors.* 1957. New York and London; Wiley

Hunter, L. P. *Handbook of Semiconductor Electronics* 2nd ed. 1962. New York and London; McGraw-Hill

INDEX

INDEX

INDEX

INDEX

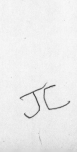